The
Book
Reviewer
Yellow Pages

A Directory of 200 Book Bloggers,
40 Blog Tour Organizers and
32 Book Review Businesses
Specializing in Indie-Published Books

9TH EDITION

CARLSBAD, CALIFORNIA

The Book Reviewer Yellow Pages:
A Directory of 200 Book Bloggers,
40 Blog Tour Organizers and 32 Book Review Businesses
Specializing in Indie-Published Books
9th Edition

© 2017 Sellbox Inc., All Rights Reserved.
Published by PartnerPress.org | Carlsbad, California
Publishing services provided by AuthorImprints, AuthorImprints.com.
Image of typewriter on cover by Florian Klauer.

Group or volume discounts available by contacting:
www.BookReviewerYellowPages.com

978-1-944098-08-7 (Paperback)
978-1-944098-09-4 (eBook)

"I will 'boom' it judiciously."
—*Jennie Churchill's promise to her son Winston,*
after reading his first book.

Table of Contents

Introduction 1

Part 1   Book Bloggers 5

Introduction 7

Quick start guide.. 8

No specific submission instructions? Write a great query email 9

Author etiquette: the art of approaching book bloggers................. 10

FAQ: frequently asked questions.................... 12

Book Blogger Listing Key 14

Book Blogger Listings 16

Part 2   Blog Tour Organizers 137

Introduction 139

Avoid scheduling overlapping promotions....................141

Less than flattering reviews 142

Tour Organizer Listing Key 143

Tour Organizer Listings............................145

Part 3   Review Businesses 169

Introduction 171

Traditional (no fee) 174

Fee-only 182

Hybrid 193

Services 201

Part 4 Resources **207**
   Reviewer Outreach Checklist 209
   Handling Negative Reviews 211
   Understanding Amazon's Terms of Service 215
   Professionally published books attract more reviewers 219

Index **227**
   Fiction Reviewers by Category 229
   Nonfiction Reviewers by Category 240
   Considers Most Fiction 244
   Considers Most Nonfiction 245
   Accepts Non-English Titles 245
   Accepts Audiobooks 246
   Review Businesses 246

Acknowledgments **247**

About *The Book Reviewer Yellow Pages* **248**

Readers are invited to download our free
Reviewer Outreach Log and Checklist,
and additional sample pitch emails, by visiting
http://breve.link/e9bonus.
More details are found in *Part 4, Resources.*

Introduction

It's a fact of book marketing that book reviews sell books, now more than ever. In the pre-Internet days—before most books were sold online like they are today—the local bookstore, newspapers, magazines, and television told us what was worth reading. Today, it's the written and often starred review, and nearly always found online with the book.

The purpose of **The Book Reviewer Yellow Pages** is to make it easier for you to find book reviewers. Specifically, individuals and businesses that review self- or independent-published books.

About the 9th Edition

This new edition has been completely redesigned based on reader feedback. It is divided into four parts, followed by seven indexes to help you quickly find specific book bloggers by key attributes.

All listing information is accurate as of October 2017. Please notify us of any updates or corrections so we can incorporate them into the 10th edition.

Part 1, Book Bloggers. Two hundred book blogger profiles in alphabetical order. This is where you'll find our recommended author etiquette, FAQs, and a quick-start guide.

Part 2, Blog Tour Organizers. Forty book blog tour organizers, also in alphabetical order. Virtual book tours continue to be a popular and effective tool to publicize your book. However, organizing a tour can be time consuming, especially for the first-time or occasionally-publishing author. A blog tour organizer manages a virtual tour on your behalf, usually for a small fee (but sometimes for free).

All tour managers listed in our directory say they can help you find book reviewers. Most also offer additional marketing and publishing services.

Part 3, Review Businesses. This is a new section for this edition in recognition that:

- There has been a rapid expansion of businesses that provide reviews or review services for a fee. This is not against any company's terms of service *so long as those terms are followed.* (See the article in Part 4, Understanding Amazon's Terms of Service.)

- Self- and indie-published books are becoming more respected, and eligible for trade reviews.

The 32 Review Businesses are further divided into four categories: Traditional (no fees), Fee-Only, Hybrid (traditional and fee), and Services.

Part 4, Resources. The information in this section applies to anyone proactively seeking book reviews. Be sure to read it all before turning to the specific advice for using Parts 1, 2, and 3.

1. Our **Reviewer Outreach Checklist** helps you prepare to contact reviewers. We outline the data necessary for tracking progress, and recommended information to assemble before you begin contacting prospective reviewers. These are also available in template form for downloading from our website.

2. We include Alex Foster's **Handling Negative Reviews,** excerpted from his book *Kindle Reviews.* We include it here with some of our own anecdotes to help set your expectations about soliciting book reviews.

3. No book about getting reviews would be complete without calling attention to Amazon's terms of service. Avoid heartache, wasted efforts, and clear up any misconceptions by reading **Understanding Amazon's Terms of Service.**

4. Teri Rider's article titled **Impress Reviewers with a Professional-Looking Book** is based on her contributions to the Advocacy Committee for the Independent Book Publishers Association (IBPA). Most reviewers, and certainly many listed in the Review

Businesses listings, evaluate the presentation of a book before deciding whether to review it. Teri's article describes in practical terms how to publish a quality book as defined in the *IBPA Industry Standards Checklist for a Professionally Published Book.*

Book reviewers of all types cite book quality—
writing and presentation—as the number one
consideration before accepting a book for review, or
the reason why they did not finish reading a book.

About the indexes

Bloggers define their reading interests by audience profile, subject matter interest, or both.

- Examples of audience profiles are: adult books, children's books, LGBTQ, middle grade, new adult (NA), and young adult (YA)

- Subject-matter interests are genres or topics that can be focused on one or more audience profile

  › For example, a book described as romance will be tailored to an audience profile.

Our two categories indexes reflect the stated interest of the blogger who may or may not have shared both attributes of their reading interests. Use the index to look up the audience and/or subject category for your book, then visit the blogger's profile. If they appear to be a match, visit the blogger's website to confirm.

Keep in mind that most reviewers will consider books on a case-by-case basis. This is especially true for fiction.

Part 1
Book Bloggers

Introduction

There are three key things to know about contacting the book bloggers in this directory.

1. They will *consider* your book for review. A listing in this directory does not guarantee that they will review your book.

2. Their requirements are *subject to change*. This is especially true for their availability. Unlike the reviewers in Part 3, Review Businesses, these book bloggers review books as a hobby and often have more books on hand than they have time to read.

3. Never, ever, send a book unless they ask for it.

All the reviewers in this edition's book blogger section are currently accepting self- and indie-published books. As mentioned, their availability to read and review your book will vary and they've given us estimated turnaround times noted in each listing. If it says *inquire*, that means they can't commit to a fixed time frame or they are currently (as of October 2017) not accepting books but expect to in the near future.

Three more general points about improving your book's chances of being accepted for a review.

1. *Quality is paramount*, especially writing quality. Unedited books will be discovered if they even make it past the consideration stage. Worse, the reviewer may express his or her dissatisfaction publicly in the review.

2. *Follow their directions* about submitting a book for consideration. Their blog, their rules. Read Author Etiquette for more advice.

3. Contact bloggers *30-90 days before* your book's release date to improve your chances of being accepted. (It's also just good marketing!) If that is not possible, be flexible with your expectations.

Quick start guide

1. Create a process and recordkeeping system for tracking who you plan to contact, and the status of each request. See our Reviewer Outreach Checklist in Part 4.

2. Assemble your book's details. (Also explained in the Reviewer Outreach Checklist in Part 4.)

3. Turn to the index and look up reviewers by the categories of books they review. Use the other indexes, if relevant.

4. Using this directory, research three to five bloggers to start. See our Book Blogger Listing Key in this section if you need help interpreting the listings.

5. Now visit their website to review their submission requirements. Look at the website's menu or for terms like "review policy," "review submissions," or their about or contact pages for instructions. **Do not to contact bloggers unless your book matches their interest.** Never mass email (spam) reviewers.

6. Record the ones you plan to contact (step 1), and contact them according to their instructions. Follow up according to their instructions.

7. Repeat steps 3-5 as you have time. There is no advantage to blasting out dozens of queries in one sitting. In fact, contacting bloggers in smaller batches will help you keep better track of conversations and be more human in your outreach.

This is essentially a sales process; you are trying to convince these reviewers that your book is worth their time to read.

No specific submission instructions? Write a great query email

Some blogs do not have submission instructions so your only choice is to send an email, or fill out their contact form. Putting our marketing hat on, we're going to send a message that respects their time, and gets their attention.

- **Subject line:** This is the most important thing you'll write. Say "Book review query" and then as few words as possible describing your book relative to their interests. (The best indicator of their interests are their past book reviews.)

- **Addressing/salutation:** Use their first name, not sir/madam or "Dear Blogger." Their social media accounts, or comments on the site are good places to look for first names.

- **Message body:** Introduce the book in a way that appeals to their interests. Make it easy to read, and to the point without extraneous details. If your book is similar to a book they previously reviewed, mention it. If you have a notable blurb, include it. Include a link to the cover if possible—perhaps the book is on Amazon, or there is an image on your website. (But no attachments at this stage!)

- **Signature block:** Your name, relationship to the book, a link to your website, and your email address.

- **Proof:** Check spelling and grammar. This is a reflection on your book. Don't use emojis, slang, or acronyms like LOL.

PUTTING IT ALL TOGETHER

> [Subject line] Book review query: WW2 alt fiction with romantic interludes
>
> Dear Jen,
>
> I found your blog in *The Book Reviewer Yellow Pages* and understand you enjoy romantic alternative fiction books. I'm excited to submit *Shadows and Joy*, a behind-the-warfront romp between two lovers from opposite sides of the war.

It is a 312-page read and available in paperback, Mobi, EPUB or PDF—your choice. I'm flexible on dates but my release date is [50 days from now].

[reader blurb if you have one, for example: "Jane Doe from Doe Reviews said 'Shadows and Joy was unlike any other historical fiction book I've read. Fast paced, believable, and titillating. Well-written too.'"]

You can click here to see the cover: [link to book on John Doe's website]. I also have an excerpt available here: [link to except on John Doe's website]

Can I answer any questions, or send you a copy? If so, please tell me what you require.

Thank you for your time,

John Doe
Author of Shadows and Joy
www.authorwebsite.com
Johndoe@gmail.com

Note: additional sample query emails are included in the free download. Visit http://breve.link/e9bonus for details.

Author etiquette: the art of approaching book bloggers

1. **Approach only those bloggers interested in your book's category.** Use our directory to narrow down your potential reviewers. Then read their submission requirements *before* sending a query. If you don't follow their directions, most will delete your email and never reply. Reaching beyond your book's category will not get you reviews—don't waste your time.

2. **Quality matters.** Reviewers are inundated with books to read. Some have stopped reviewing self-published books due to poor quality, others because of self-published authors not following

their requirements (see #1). A polished book is more likely to be considered and gain a favorable review.

3. **Make your pitch friendly, respectful, and to the point.** Address them using their name. It is a sign you read their blog. Follow their instructions—never send a generic query or form letter. And never, ever send mass emails.

4. **Lead times can be long and schedules tight.** Bloggers are essentially volunteering to read your book. Manage your own expectations—plan ahead, be flexible, and don't be demanding. Many bloggers clearly state how or if you should follow up after you've made initial contact.

5. **The reviewer is doing you a favor.** Make getting your book free, easy, and convenient. Do not expect the reviewer to buy your book, or pay for shipping. (They have too many other books to read! See #2.)

6. **Don't expect them to love your book.** Some won't post a critical review and instead will provide feedback on why they didn't like it. Some won't explain themselves. Some will indeed post their honest opinion. Avoid potential issues by approaching only those reviewers who enjoy your genre (see #1, and read Handling Negative Reviews in Part 4).

7. **Be gracious and say thank you no matter the outcome.** Remember, you are building relationships because you might be back with a follow-up book. Kindness, just like rude comments, has a way of living forever on social media and on websites. Reviewers can and do research authors.

In summary, follow the Golden Rule.

Treat reviewers the way you would like to be treated.

FAQ: frequently asked questions

An occasional frustration we hear is that listed reviewers are too busy to receive unsolicited requests or the reviewer may simply be disinterested. That's simply the nature of book blogging so move on to the next book blog. Here are a few other questions we get:

Q: How do I know whether a blogger is worth my time to contact?

First, accept that it is the blogger who is doing you a favor, not the other way around. But given your limited time, and assuming a large source of blogs to approach, there are a few key indicators of high-quality book bloggers. (Note: no one metric tells the complete story—consider them collectively and use your best judgment. Also keep in mind that a blogger who is just starting out may become more popular in time, so starting a relationship with him or her now will benefit you in the long term.)

- How frequently do they post reviews? High frequency of quality posts often leads to more visitors ("reach").

- What is the website's Alexa ranking? The lower the number, the more popular the website. (https://www.alexa.com/siteinfo)

- How many social media followers do they have on their different platforms?

- How high is their Klout score? (https://klout.com/)

- Does the website have a high number of inbound links, and how high is the Domain Authority? Both are measured by the free Moz Open Site Explorer (https://moz.com/researchtools/ose/).

Q: What does mean when a listing says "most fiction considered"?

Some reviewers will read anything that captures their imagination, or their reading interests exceed the number of categories we can list. You'll see this phrase next to the Fiction category heading. These reviewers are listed in their own index.

Q: What is the difference between Kindle and Mobi?

Many reviewers use the terms interchangeably to refer to eBooks that are read using Kindle apps, Kindle devices, and Fire tablets. Anyone can read a Mobi file format using a free Kindle reading app from Amazon. Some bloggers say Kindle to mean they prefer you to gift them your book from the Kindle store. Ask if it isn't clear.

Q: This is taking a lot of time. Is there an easier/faster way to get reviews?

No, unless you have a budget. Alternatively, Tour Organizers will present your book to their list of reviewers for a fee. And many of the businesses in Part 3, Review Businesses review books for a fee. You either spend your time, or money, the choice is yours.

Book Blogger Listing Key

The numbers below refer to the numbers on the following page. As a reminder, all listing information was provided by the blogger.

- Questions about the reviewer's listing information must be addressed to the reviewer.
- Always review the blogger's current submission information before contacting them.

Information is subject to change without notice. Follow our advice about author etiquette.

 Use this code when reporting errors or updates for this specific listing via the GIVE updates link in the footer.

 The website link for the blog.

 Contact name (when provided) is followed by the reviewer's preferred method of contact.

 eBooks: The eBook file formats the blogger accepts. Note that many bloggers will use "Kindle" to refer to the Mobi file format, but they could also refer to Kindle books you could gift them. Always inquire if you are unsure.

 Audiobooks: A "Yes" indicates they accept them, a "No," specifically not. If blank, we suggest you inquire because this format is gaining in popularity.

 Fees/services: A "Yes" means a blogger provides publishing services, advertising, or accepts fees for reviewing books more quickly.

 Tours: Bloggers that are Tour Hosts for Tour Organizers have a "Yes" in this field.

 Approximate turnaround time: How long they typically take to review a book.

 Where reviews are posted: The locations, besides their website, where they post reviews. "+ Social" means they also promote it via one or more social media platforms.

Categories: What the blogger has told us they are interested in reading, or not reading. If blank, the information was not provided. Note that their category names may or may not match the category names that stores use to sell books.

- NA=New Adult, YA=Young Adult

 From the reviewer: A short bio or personal statement shared by the blogger.

Stephanie's Book Reports (B9-192) ← ✪

http://www.stephaniesbookreports.com ← ✪

Stephanie | http://www.stephaniesbookreports.com/review-request ↖✪

eBooks	Audiobooks	Fees/Services	Tours
Kindle ✪	Yes ✪	Yes ✪	Yes ✪

Approximate turnaround time: ~1 mo ← ✪

Where reviews are posted: Amazon, Goodreads, +Social — ✪

Languages: English

 ✪

CATEGORIES ← ✪

- **Fiction:** NA, Romance, YA
- **Nonfiction:**
- **Excluded:** Biography, Comics, Nonfiction

From the reviewer: I am a stay-at-home mom who loves to read. I started my blog to help readers find the books they're looking for. Stephanie's Book Reports strives to review as many books in a month as possible. Reviewers mostly take e-books, but they also will take galley and audiobooks for review as well.

3 Partners in Shopping (B9-001)

http://3partnersinshopping.blogspot.com
Debra Gaudette | http://3partnersinshopping.blogspot.com

eBooks	Audiobooks	Fees/Services	Tours
Kindle	Yes	Inquire	Yes

Approximate turnaround time: 6 wk
Where reviews are posted: Amazon, BlogLovin, +Social
Languages: English

CATEGORIES
- **Fiction:** Contemporary, Dystopian, Fantasy, Graphic Novels, Historical Fiction, Romance
- **Nonfiction:** Yes, Cookbooks, Crafting, Memoirs, Self-Help
- **Excluded:** Erotica

From the reviewer: I am a grandmother who loves to read and share this love with others.

A Different Kind of Read (B9-230)

http://www.adifferentkindofread.com
Barbara Gipson | barbaragipson@earthlink.net

eBooks	Audiobooks	Fees/Services	Tours
EPUB, PDF		Yes	No

Approximate turnaround time: Inquire
Where reviews are posted: Amazon, Goodreads, Pinterest
Languages: English

CATEGORIES
- **Fiction:** Adventure, Fantasy, Fiction-General, Historical Fiction, Mystery
- **Nonfiction:** Yes
- **Excluded:** Erotica, Horror, War

From the reviewer: I am a self published author who noticed that many Blogs did not like to review books written by Independent Authors. In an effort to give back to those that helped me, I give free reviews to all authors and publishing companies.

A Thousand Words a Million Books (B9-002)

http://athousandwordsamillionbooks.blogspot.in

Aditi Nichani | athousandwordsamillionbooks@gmail.com

eBooks	Audiobooks	Fees/Services	Tours
Mobi, EPUB		Inquire	Yes

Approximate turnaround time: 2 wk to 1 mo

Where reviews are posted: Amazon, Goodreads, BN, Wordery

Languages: English

CATEGORIES

- **Fiction:** YA
- **Nonfiction:** No
- **Excluded:** Erotica, Religion

From the reviewer: I'm a college freshman who loves young adult books. I do prefer print copies of books, but I accept e-books as well. I'm really looking forward to connecting with new authors!

A Writer's Journal (B9-003)

http://dalycedomain.com/

D. Alyce Domain | Use website contact form

eBooks	Audiobooks	Fees/Services	Tours
Kindle, iBooks, PDF		Inquire	Yes

Approximate turnaround time: 2-3 wk

Where reviews are posted: Amazon, Goodreads

Languages: English

CATEGORIES

- **Fiction:** Christian Fiction, Contemporary Romance, Fantasy, Gothic Romance, Historical Romance, Mystery, Paranormal Romance, Science Fiction, Suspense
- **Nonfiction:** No
- **Excluded:** Children's, Comics, Erotica, Horror, LGBTQ, Political Themed

From the reviewer: I wear many hats. Avid Reader. Reviewer. Indie Author. Book Blogger. Desktop Publisher. Proof-reader and editor. Boutique Owner. Fashionista. Jewelry Designer. Houstonian. Christian.

A.M. Aitken (B9-004)

https://www.amaitken.com/category/book-review/
Ale | https://www.amaitken.com/review-contact/

eBooks	Audiobooks	Fees/Services	Tours
Kindle		Inquire	No

Approximate turnaround time: 2-3 mo
Where reviews are posted: Goodreads, Medium
Languages: English, German

CATEGORIES

- **Fiction:** Fiction-General, Historical Fiction, Mystery, Paranormal, Science Fiction, Thriller, YA
- **Nonfiction:** Yes, Business, IT, Memoirs
- **Excluded:** Comics, Erotica

From the reviewer: I'm a software developer who is an author and avid reader in his spare time. I love reading YA or anything to do with magicians. I also like reading stories that will drive some sort of emotional response in me.

A.O. Chika Book Blog (B9-005)

http://aochikabooks.com/
A.O. Chika | http://aochikabooks.com/contact/review-request/

eBooks	Audiobooks	Fees/Services	Tours
Kindle, EPUB	No	No	Yes

Approximate turnaround time: 2-4 wk
Where reviews are posted: Goodreads, +Social
Languages: English

CATEGORIES

- **Fiction:** LGBTQ (all genres except as noted)
- **Nonfiction:** No
- **Excluded:** Horror

From the reviewer: I'm a PR and Growth marketing expert who loves reading LGBT books as a way to relax from the pressure and stress at work.

All the Things In Between (B9-006)

http://allthethingsinbetween.net

Ms. Ali Cat and Simona | bloggers@allthethingsinbetween.net

eBooks	Audiobooks	Fees/Services	Tours
Yes	No	No	Inquire

Approximate turnaround time: Inquire

Where reviews are posted: Amazon, Goodreads, BN, Edelweiss, Google Play Books, LibraryThing, NetGalley, +Social

Languages: English, Italian

CATEGORIES

- **Fiction:** Adventure, Fantasy, Science Fiction, YA
- **Nonfiction:** Yes, Biography, Cultural, Health & Fitness, History, Instructional, Lifestyle, Memoirs, Politics, Psychology, Religious, Travel
- **Excluded:** Inquire

From the reviewer: Ali is a writer, reader, and influencer who reviews books first--followed secondly by people, places, and things. Coffee, making lists, Panic! At The Disco, Black Veil Brides and Jung Joon Young make her happy; add her four beastly besties and her guy into the equation, life becomes sublime. Ali is all over shifter stories, loves the jackass heroes with too much attitude, and has foregone reading the last book in some of her favorite series so they never end. Simona lives in Sicily, Italy. She loves languages, classic rock, and has an addiction to chocolate. She shamelessly lacks prejudice regarding what she picks up to read but counts Margaret Mitchell, Neil Gaiman, and Lev Tolstoj amongst her favorites. Simona's spirit animal is a monkey that she calls Louie.

Always Trust in Books (B9-008)

http://www.alwaystrustinbooks.wordpress.com
Stuart | stuartsimpson1990@gmail.com

eBooks	Audiobooks	Fees/Services	Tours
No		No	Yes

Approximate turnaround time: 3 mo
Where reviews are posted: Amazon, Goodreads, Bookbridgr, Bloglovin, +Social
Languages: English

CATEGORIES

- **Fiction:** Classics, Crime, Fantasy, Horror, Science Fiction, Thriller
- **Nonfiction:** Yes, Law (in particular)
- **Excluded:** Erotica, Poetry, Romance, YA

From the reviewer: I am a married father of two boys. I read and review in my spare time.

Amazeballs Book Addicts (B9-009)

http://amazeballsbookaddicts.blogspot.com
Gia and Tabitha | amazeballsbookaddicts@yahoo.com

eBooks	Audiobooks	Fees/Services	Tours
Kindle		No	Yes

Approximate turnaround time: 4-6 wk
Where reviews are posted: Amazon, Goodreads, +Social
Languages: English

CATEGORIES

- **Fiction:** Crime, Erotica, Fantasy, Historical Fiction, Horror, Murder Mystery, Science Fiction, Urban Fantasy
- **Nonfiction:** No
- **Excluded:** Non-Fiction

From the reviewer: We are two friends who love books. We love to review books and post about our favorite authors and books.

Ana's Attic Book Blog (B9-010)

http://anasattic.com

Ana | http://anasattic.com/review-policy-and-contact-info/

eBooks	Audiobooks	Fees/Services	Tours
Kindle	Yes	Yes	No

Approximate turnaround time: 1-2 mo
Where reviews are posted: Amazon, Goodreads
Languages: English

CATEGORIES

- **Fiction:** Erotica, Contemporary Romance, Romance, NA, Women's Fiction
- **Nonfiction:** No
- **Excluded:** Christian, Dystopian, Manga, Nonfiction

From the reviewer: I started Ana's Attic in 2012 as "What to Read After Fifty Shades", and expanded from there. I also do Wicked Book Weekend and Starting on Monday.

Audiothing (B9-011)

http://audiothing.blogspot.com.au

Bec Stokes | towanblystry@gmail.com

eBooks	Audiobooks	Fees/Services	Tours
No	Yes	Inquire	No

Approximate turnaround time: 6-8 wk
Where reviews are posted: Amazon, Goodreads, Audible, +Social
Languages: English

CATEGORIES

- **Fiction:** Crime, Mystery
- **Nonfiction:** Yes, Cookbooks, Crafting, Crochet, Home Décor, Memoirs, Music
- **Excluded:** Erotica, Graphically Violent, Horror, Legal Procedurals, Science Fiction

From the reviewer: I am a recently retired nurse educator. I love to read. I enjoy helping to promote good books.

Author Unpublished (B9-012)

http://authorunpublished.wordpress.com
Cary Morton | https://authorunpublished.
wordpress.com/reviewed-rated/

eBooks	Audiobooks	Fees/Services	Tours
Any		Inquire	Inquire

Approximate turnaround time: Inquire
Where reviews are posted: Amazon, Goodreads, +Social
Languages: English

CATEGORIES
- **Fiction:** Crime, Fantasy, Historical Fiction, Middle Grade, Mystery, NA, Paranormal, Romance, Science Fiction, Suspense, YA
- **Nonfiction:** Rarely, Memoirs
- **Excluded:** Flash Fiction, Novellas, Poetry, Short Fiction

From the reviewer: I am an avid reader, freelance copy editor, artist, and book reviewer! I'm a huge fan of the romance genre, and unapologetic about it. I post reviews weekly, and love to discuss writing and reading fiction!

b00k r3vi3ws (B9-013)

http://www.ddsreviews.in
Debdatta D. Sahay | http://bit.ly/2cvIQVI

eBooks	Audiobooks	Fees/Services	Tours
Kindle		No	Yes

Approximate turnaround time: 8-10 wk
Where reviews are posted: Amazon, Goodreads
Languages: English

CATEGORIES
- **Fiction:** Contemporary, Dystopian, Fantasy, Mystery, Paranormal, Thriller, YA
- **Nonfiction:** No
- **Excluded:** Erotica, Non-Fiction, Self-Help

From the reviewer: My name is Debdatta Dasgupta Sahay and I am a book addict from India. When I am not reading, I am driving people nuts by talking about them. I used to be a Human Resource Professional with 6 years of work experience under my belt. I am currently pursuing my 2nd Post-Graduate degree in Mass Communication and Journalism.

Bad Bird Reads (B9-014)

http://badbirdreads.com/
Jennifer | badbirdreads@yahoo.com

eBooks	Audiobooks	Fees/Services	Tours
Kindle, Mobi		No	Yes

Approximate turnaround time: 3 mo
Where reviews are posted: Amazon, Goodreads
Languages: English

CATEGORIES

- **Fiction:** Adventure, Dystopian, Erotica, Fantasy, Historical Fiction, Horror, NA, Paranormal, Romance, Science Fiction, Suspense, Urban Fantasy, YA
- **Nonfiction:** No
- **Excluded:** Christian, Nonfiction

From the reviewer: I love reading as much as I can. My passion is reading. I love to try new books and new authors. I try to run one giveaway a week and I keep my blog fresh with a variety of posts.

Barbara's Book Reviews (B9-231)

http://www.adifferentkindofread.com
Barbara Gipson | barbaragipson@earthlink.net

eBooks	Audiobooks	Fees/Services	Tours
EPUB, PDF		Yes	No

Approximate turnaround time: Inquire
Where reviews are posted: Amazon, Goodreads, LibraryThing, Pinterest
Languages: English

CATEGORIES

- **Fiction:** Fantasy, Fantasy, Historical Fiction, Humor, Mystery, Romance, Science Fiction
- **Nonfiction:** Yes, Religion, War
- **Excluded:** Erotica, Horror, Religion, War

From the reviewer: I am an author/editor and book reviewer. I review both fiction and non-fiction books in the following genres: mystery, adventure, fantasy, humor, historical, romance, and science fiction. Primarily, I prefer children and young adult books, but I also review adult. I'm looking for books that feature unique, ethnic, or special needs characters or storylines.

GIVE updates: http://breve.link/e9give   GET updates: http://breve.link/e9get

Barnsey's Books (B9-015)

http://barnseybooks.blogspot.co.uk
Lynne Barnes | Use website contact form

eBooks	Audiobooks	Fees/Services	Tours
Kindle, Mobi		No	No

Approximate turnaround time: Inquire
Where reviews are posted: Amazon, Goodreads, Waterstones, BN, Bookbridgr, +Social
Languages: English

CATEGORIES

- **Fiction:** Action, Adventure, Crime, Horror, Mystery, Science Fiction, Thriller
- **Nonfiction:** No
- **Excluded:** Children's, Erotica, YA

From the reviewer: I am a female, British reviewer currently living in Worcestershire. My working background is in the British media industry where I was employed for over two decades at an international Media Monitoring and Press Clippings business. Through my working experience I fully understand the impact publicity and reviews can have upon reaching a wider audience. Reading was a major part of my working life and has always played a massive part of who I am.

Bea's Book Nook (B9-017)

http://beasbooknook.blogspot.com
Bea, Jax, and Steph | http://tinyurl.com/yblkfm7f

eBooks	Audiobooks	Fees/Services	Tours
Kindle, EPUB	Yes	Inquire	Yes

Approximate turnaround time: 1-2 mo
Where reviews are posted: Amazon, Goodreads, +Social
Languages: English

CATEGORIES

- **Fiction:** Fantasy, Mystery, Romance, Urban Fantasy, Women's Fiction, YA
- **Nonfiction:** Yes, Child Growth, Cookbooks, Crafting, Literacy
- **Excluded:** Biography, Business, Memoirs, Poetry, Self-Help

From the reviewer: I'm a woman in my 50s who love to read and to talk about books. I teach toddlers, craft soaps and other bath products, and like to chill out with a good book and a movie.

Beck Valley Books (B9-018)

http://beckvalleybooks.blogspot.com
Sharon Martin | beckvalleybooks@gmail.com

eBooks	Audiobooks	Fees/Services	Tours
No		Yes	Yes

Approximate turnaround time: 1-2 mo
Where reviews are posted: Shares widely; inquire
Languages: English

CATEGORIES

- **Fiction:** Children's, Fiction-General, Mystery, Romance, Suspense, Thriller
- **Nonfiction:** Yes, Cookbooks, Memoirs, Self-Help
- **Excluded:** Erotica, Horror, Science Fiction

From the reviewer: I am a mum of two sporty teenage boys who runs her blog and tour company from home. Our passion for books started our blog. We love being part of the book blogging community.

Belle's Book Blog (B9-242)

https://www.bellesbookblog.net
Belle Boudreaux | https://www.bellesbookblog.net/contact

eBooks	Audiobooks	Fees/Services	Tours
Kindle, Mobi, EPUB, PDF	No	No	No

Approximate turnaround time: <2 wk
Where reviews are posted: Goodreads, BN
Languages: English

CATEGORIES

- **Fiction:** Contemporary Romance, Middle Grade, YA
- **Nonfiction:** No
- **Excluded:** Erotica

From the reviewer: I review young adult books of all kinds on my blog, www.bellesbookblog.net (although I do have a soft spot for YA contemporary romances!). I usually post my reviews every Monday, but I can schedule another day with you if preferred. If you have any questions, or you want me to do a review on your book, you can fill out a form on my Contact page (https://www.bellesbookblog.net/contact) or send an email to me at belles-bookblog@europe.com.

Bibliofreak.net (B9-019)

http://www.bibliofreak.net
Matthew Selwyn | http://www.bibliofreak.net/p/review-policy.html

eBooks	Audiobooks	Fees/Services	Tours
Mobi, EPUB		Yes	No

Approximate turnaround time: Inquire
Where reviews are posted: Goodreads, +Social
Languages: English

CATEGORIES

- **Fiction:** Fiction-General, Literary Fiction
- **Nonfiction:** Yes
- **Excluded:** Erotica, Chick Lit

From the reviewer: If you're interested in me (and why wouldn't you be?), you can read a little about my background here: http://www.bibliofreak.net/p/about.html.

Bibliophile Mystery (B9-020)

http://bibliophilemystery.blogspot.ro/
Cristina and Andra | bibliophilemystery@gmail.com

eBooks	Audiobooks	Fees/Services	Tours
Kindle		Yes	Yes

Approximate turnaround time: 1-2 mo
Where reviews are posted: Amazon, Goodreads, +Social
Languages: English

CATEGORIES

- **Fiction:** Contemporary Romance, Dystopian, Historical Fiction, NA, Paranormal, Urban Fantasy, YA
- **Nonfiction:** No
- **Excluded:** Christian, Erotica

From the reviewer: We love to help promote great stories from new authors. Clean covers, please.

Bite Into Books (B9-021)

http://biteintobooks.blogspot.com
Esther | Contact via Goodreads

eBooks	**Audiobooks**	**Fees/Services**	**Tours**
Kindle		Yes	No

Approximate turnaround time: 2-3 mo
Where reviews are posted: Goodreads
Languages: English, Dutch

CATEGORIES

- **Fiction:** Chick Lit, Contemporary, Crime, Erotica, Fantasy, Fiction-General, Horror, Mystery, Paranormal, Romance, Science Fiction, Thriller, YA
- **Nonfiction:** No
- **Excluded:** Poetry, Self-Help

From the reviewer: My name is Esther. I'm a 25 year old teacher from The Netherlands. Next to working 40 hours a week, I love to read, workout, travel and bake. You can call me a book junkie. I read somewhere near 10 books a month and I ADORE my books. I think I might own 150 books, and I'm still counting! I've been reviewing my books on Goodreads for a year now. In 2017, I started a blog to spread teh word about all the books I read and to share my opinion.

Bitten By Love (B9-022)

http://www.bittenbylovereviews.com
Jenni Dinh | bittenbylovereviews@gmail.com

eBooks	Audiobooks	Fees/Services	Tours
EPUB, PDF		Yes	Yes

Approximate turnaround time: 1-2 mo
Where reviews are posted: Amazon, Goodreads, BN, +Social
Languages: English

CATEGORIES

- **Fiction:** Contemporary Romance, Erotica, Fantasy, Historical Romance, LGBTQ, Paranormal Romance, Romance, Science Fiction, Urban Fantasy, Western Romance, YA
- **Nonfiction:** No
- **Excluded:** Bestiality, Necrophilia, Pedophilia, Physical Abuse, Rape

From the reviewer: Bitten By Love and Delta Strategic Planning (DSP) is among the leading Blog Editorial Review and Virtual Administrative Assistant independent agencies. The company is led by Jennilinh Dinh, owner and director. As part of its structures, DSP and BBL is recognized for helping independent contractors and small business owners with daily customer services, administrative tasks, book reviews, publicity, and marketing execution. Jenni offers her clients the benefits of ten years' experience in retail management, six years as a business analyst in annuities and insurance with a global Fortune 500 company, and several years as a virtual assistant and publicist for local business owners and writers, including New York Times, USA, and Amazon bestselling authors.

Blogger Nicole (B9-023)

http://www.bloggernicole.com
Nicole Wright | http://bloggernicole.com/contact/

eBooks	**Audiobooks**	**Fees/Services**	**Tours**
Kindle		No	Yes

Approximate turnaround time: 1-2 mo
Where reviews are posted: Amazon, Goodreads
Languages: English

CATEGORIES

- **Fiction:** Cozy Mystery, Romance
- **Nonfiction:** No
- **Excluded:** Erotica, Nonfiction

From the reviewer: I am a mother of two. I love to read, blog, and run giveaways.

Book Babble (B9-024)

http://memesandfiction.blogspot.com
Teresa Kander | eeyoregirl2009@aol.com

eBooks	**Audiobooks**	**Fees/Services**	**Tours**
Kindle		No	Yes

Approximate turnaround time: 1-2 mo
Where reviews are posted: Amazon, Goodreads, +Social
Languages: English

CATEGORIES

- **Fiction:** Amish, Chick Lit, Children's, Cozy Mystery, Dystopian, Poetry, Suspense, Thriller, YA
- **Nonfiction:** Yes, Biography, Christian, Cookbooks, Memoirs, True Crime
- **Excluded:** Erotica, Gore, Harlequin-Type Romance, Political Nonfiction, Profanity, Science Fiction, Violence, Western

From the reviewer: I'm a writer and poet who loves to read and share my opinions of books with other people.

Book Bangs (B9-025)

http://www.bookbangs.com/
Lace and Lana | Use website contact form

eBooks	Audiobooks	Fees/Services	Tours
Kindle		Yes	Yes

Approximate turnaround time: 6 wk
Where reviews are posted: Amazon, +Social
Languages: English

CATEGORIES

- **Fiction:** NA, Paranormal, Romance
- **Nonfiction:** No
- **Excluded:** Dystopian, Erotica, Fantasy, Science Fiction

From the reviewer: Lace is a mother of a toddler and a teenager who loves to read and help new authors spread the word about their books.

Book Explosions (B9-026)

http://www.crystalcrichlow.com/book-explosions-reviews
Crystal and Margaret
http://www.crystalcrichlow.com/review-submission-guidelines.html

eBooks	Audiobooks	Fees/Services	Tours
Kindle, PDF		No	No

Approximate turnaround time: 4-8 wk
Where reviews are posted: Amazon, Goodreads, +Social
Languages: English

CATEGORIES

- **Fiction:** Children's, Dystopian, Middle Grade, YA
- **Nonfiction:** No
- **Excluded:** Biographies, Erotica, Paranormal, Politics, Religious, Self-Help

From the reviewer: I am a writer and avid book reviewer. When I'm not writing books, I spend most my time binge watching shows on Netflix. I have an unhealthy obsession with zombies. I started writing reviews because as an author, I understand that reviews are what makes an author and would like to do my part in the literary world to keep it thriving.

BOOK BLOGGERS

Book Freak (B9-027)

http://reviewsofabookmaniac.blogspot.com
Cha Delfin | http://tinyurl.com/y7bz2dj9

eBooks	Audiobooks	Fees/Services	Tours
Kindle		Yes	Yes

Approximate turnaround time: 1-2 mo
Where reviews are posted: Amazon, Goodreads, +Social
Languages: English

CATEGORIES

- **Fiction:** Contemporary Romance, NA, Regency Romance, YA
- **Nonfiction:** No
- **Excluded:** Erotica, Paranormal, Vampires

From the reviewer: I am a nurse who loves to read romance and everything-in-between.

BOOK BLOGGERS

BOOK BLOGGERS

Book Readers (B9-028)

http://bookread-mumswritings.blogspot.com/
Dee | http://tinyurl.com/y86wxwdk

eBooks	Audiobooks	Fees/Services	Tours
Kindle, Mobi		Yes	Yes

Approximate turnaround time: 4-8 wk
Where reviews are posted: Amazon, BN, Goodreads, LibraryThing, +Social
Languages: English

CATEGORIES

- **Fiction:** Adventure, Christian Fiction, Historical Fiction, Humor, Literary Fiction, Mystery, Poetry, Suspense, Thriller, YA
- **Nonfiction:** Yes, Arts, Autobiography, Biography, Culture, True Crime
- **Excluded:** Erotica, Horror, Paranormal, Romance, Western

From the reviewer: I am not an author, but love to read. When we found mum's writings, I was in heaven... reading, transcribing from handwritten to computer and starting the search and education on how to get them published. As an avid reader, I became fascinated with Mum's stories and books. All her writings were hand written on legal size paper or note books, on both sides of the paper. I began reading some of the 50 plus short stories and four books. After reading a few, I was hooked, Mum's writing was not the clearest, however, I had set myself the challenge and was going to follow through. At times, I was frustrated with Mum's hand writing. The first book was published 2008 "Ladies of Class" now Mum's second book "The Poison Pen" is now published April 30th 2014 http://vinspirepublishing.com

Book Referees (B9-029)

http://www.bookreferees.org
Orsayer Simmons | http://www.bookreferees.org

eBooks	Audiobooks	Fees/Services	Tours
Kindle		Yes	Yes

Approximate turnaround time: 1-3 mo
Where reviews are posted: Amazon, Goodreads, BN, +Social
Languages: English

CATEGORIES

- **Fiction:** Most fiction considered
- **Nonfiction:** Yes
- **Excluded:** None specified

From the reviewer: Book Referees is an award-winning blog.

Book Review Virginia Lee (B9-030)

https://www.facebook.com/bookreviewvirginialee/
Virginia Lee | https://www.facebook.com/bookreviewvirginialee/

eBooks	Audiobooks	Fees/Services	Tours
Kindle, Mobi		No	Yes

Approximate turnaround time: 7-10 days
Where reviews are posted: Amazon, Goodreads, +Social
Languages: English

CATEGORIES

- **Fiction:** Erotica, LGBTQ, Paranormal, Romance, Science Fiction
- **Nonfiction:** No
- **Excluded:** Biography

From the reviewer: Book Review Virginia Lee Blog: we support romance authors. Be it through book reviews, cover reveal, release blitz, blog tour, and teasers.

Reviewer Yellow Pages (B9-241)

krevieweryellowpages.com/
ps://bookrevieweryellowpages.com/contact/

eBooks	Audiobooks	Fees/Services	Tours
No		Yes	No

Approximate turnaround time: Inquire
Where reviews are posted: Amazon, Goodreads
Languages: English

CATEGORIES

- **Fiction:** None
- **Nonfiction:** Yes, Internet, Marketing, Publishing, Writing
- **Excluded:** Everything except what's noted

From the reviewer: We will consider reviewing professionally edited and produced books in the noted topics. Books must be at least 10k words and avaible in paperback or hardcover, in addition to Kindle and EPUB. Special consideration is given to books submitted for consideration at least 60 days before publication date.

Book Reviews and Giveaways (B9-031)

http://bookreviewsandgiveaways.org
Jenn | kaseycocoa48@gmail.com

eBooks	Audiobooks	Fees/Services	Tours
Kindle, EPUB		Yes	No

Approximate turnaround time: Inquire
Where reviews are posted: Amazon, Goodreads, +Social
Languages: English

CATEGORIES

- **Fiction:** Most fiction considered, (Family Friendly)
- **Nonfiction:** Yes, Animals, Automobile Racing, Cookbooks, Crafting, History
- **Excluded:** Erotica

From the reviewer: My name is Jenn. I'm a single mom, college student, published poet, short story writer, animal lover, teacher, librarian, chauffeur, chef, craft-maker, and English language-loving avid book reader. Oh, and I've been told I lack a sense of humor.

Bookangel (B9-033)

http://bookangel.co.uk

Bookangel | http://bookangel.co.uk/submit-a-book/

eBooks	Audiobooks	Fees/Services	Tours
Kindle		Yes	No

Approximate turnaround time: Inquire
Where reviews are posted: Amazon, Goodreads, +Social
Languages: English

CATEGORIES

- **Fiction:** Most fiction considered
- **Nonfiction:** Yes, History, Memoirs
- **Excluded:** Erotica

From the reviewer: We're a book club, who started swapping free book suggestions, and then it grew into the site.

Bookish Outsider (B9-035)

http://bookishoutsider.blogspot.com

Fi | bookishoutsider@gmail.com

eBooks	Audiobooks	Fees/Services	Tours
Mobi, PDF		No	No

Approximate turnaround time: 6-8 wk
Where reviews are posted: Amazon, Goodreads, LibraryThing, +Social
Languages: English

CATEGORIES

- **Fiction:** Dystopian, Fairy Tales, Fantasy, Horror, Mystery, Mythology, Paranormal, Science Fiction, Steampunk, Thriller, Urban Fantasy
- **Nonfiction:** Yes, Folklore, History
- **Excluded:** Erotica, Romance

From the reviewer: Bookseller and lifelong bookworm, addicted to the library and can find a spot to read anywhere. I donate any finished copies I'm sent to my library or charity store.

Bookish Reveries (B9-036)

http://bookishreveriess.blogspot.in
Ravneet Kaur | ravneetkaur113@gmail.com

eBooks	Audiobooks	Fees/Services	Tours
Kindle		No	Inquire

Approximate turnaround time: 15 days
Where reviews are posted: Amazon, Goodreads
Languages: English, Hindi

CATEGORIES

- **Fiction:** Most fiction considered
- **Nonfiction:** Yes, Productivity, Self-Help, Start-Ups
- **Excluded:** Children's, Erotica

From the reviewer: My name is Ravneet Kaur and it goes without saying that I love reading. I like to read

Booklove (B9-037)

http://readdayandnight.blogspot.com
Rubina Bashir | readingfit25@gmail.com

eBooks	Audiobooks	Fees/Services	Tours
Kindle, Mobi, PDF		Yes	Yes

Approximate turnaround time: 2 wk
Where reviews are posted: Amazon, Goodreads, +Social
Languages: English, Hindi, Urdu, Punjabi, Indian

CATEGORIES

- **Fiction:** Fantasy, Paranormal, Children's, Middle Grade, Chick Lit, YA, NA, Horror, Mystery, Thriller
- **Nonfiction:** Yes, Biography, Cookbooks, Memoirs, Self-Help
- **Excluded:** Erotica

From the reviewer: I love to read and review books and share the goodness with others.

Bookroom Reviews (B9-038)

http://bookroomreviews.com

Dick Leonardo | dick@bookroomreviews.com

eBooks	Audiobooks	Fees/Services	Tours
Yes		Yes	Yes

Approximate turnaround time: 2-3 wk
Where reviews are posted: Social
Languages: English

CATEGORIES

- **Fiction:** Chick Lit, Children's, Romance, YA
- **Nonfiction:** Yes, Children's, Cookbooks, Crafting, Educational, Health&Fitness, Parenting
- **Excluded:** Erotica

From the reviewer: We were one of the top 15 children's book review site of 2014 also in 2016 we made this list 12 Great Book Review Sites for Indie Middle Grade Novels and 2017 made the list The Best Book Review Blogs for 2017.

Books are Love (B9-040)

http://hello-booklover.tumblr.com/

Melissa | redtide@rcn.com

eBooks	Audiobooks	Fees/Services	Tours
Kindle		No	Yes

Approximate turnaround time: 6 wk
Where reviews are posted: Amazon, Goodreads, +Social
Languages: English

CATEGORIES

- **Fiction:** Classics, Fiction-General, NA, YA
- **Nonfiction:** Yes
- **Excluded:** None

From the reviewer: Not submitted.

BOOK BLOGGERS

Books Direct (B9-041)

http://booksdirectonline.blogspot.com

Lynda Dickson | booksdirectonline@gmail.com

eBooks	Audiobooks	Fees/Services	Tours
Kindle, EPUB, PDF		Yes	Yes

Approximate turnaround time: Inquire

Where reviews are posted: Amazon, Goodreads, BN, Smashwords, +Social

Languages: English

CATEGORIES

- **Fiction:** Children's, Horror, Humor, Literary Fiction, Mystery, Thriller, YA
- **Nonfiction:** Yes, Autobiography, Biography, Children's, Cookbooks, Marketing, Memoirs, Publishing, True Crime, Writing
- **Excluded:** Erotica, Fantasy, Religious, Science Fiction, Western

From the reviewer: I love reading, promoting indie authors, and participating in blog tours. Reviewing is just a small part of what I do. I also feature author interviews, free days, giveaways, guest posts, new releases, and sales. I share all posts via my extensive social media circles. I ask that featured authors share my posts and follow me and my blog via any social media avenues available to them.

Books R Us (B9-043)

http://www.booksrusonline.com
Eileen and Melissa Burmester | http://tinyurl.com/ybfpbqj4

eBooks	Audiobooks	Fees/Services	Tours
Kindle		Yes	Yes

Approximate turnaround time: 1 mo
Where reviews are posted: Amazon, Goodreads, BN, +Social
Languages: English

CATEGORIES

- **Fiction:** Drama, Fantasy, Historical Fiction, Horror, Paranormal, Romance, YA
- **Nonfiction:** Yes, Cookbooks, Gardening, Self-Help
- **Excluded:** Erotica

From the reviewer: Welcome to Books R Us, a place for reviews, contents and other interesting tidbits. Here you can find posts on a variety of topics including books, software, food and everyday living. My blog is all about life and all of the crazy things that can happen every day. So stop by for a visit and relax for a while.

Books, Reviews, Etc. (B9-044)

http://bemiown.blogspot.com
Gayle | bemiown@yahoo.com

eBooks	Audiobooks	Fees/Services	Tours
Kindle		No	Yes

Approximate turnaround time: 3-4 wk
Where reviews are posted: Amazon, Goodreads, +Social
Languages: English

CATEGORIES

- **Fiction:** Amish, Historical Fiction, Historical Romance, Horror, Mystery, Westerns
- **Nonfiction:** Yes, Car Racing, Cookbooks, Crafting, Memoirs, True Crime
- **Excluded:** Erotica, Paranormal, Science Fiction

From the reviewer: I'm a domestic engineer and a jack of all trades. I've learned to do a bit of everything out of necessity. We will do cover reveals, interviews, tours, blasts and first chapter reveals.

BOOK BLOGGERS

Bookshipper (B9-045)

http://bookshipper.blogspot.com/
Tina | tina_avon@yahoo.com

eBooks	Audiobooks	Fees/Services	Tours
Kindle		No	No

Approximate turnaround time: 1 mo
Where reviews are posted: Amazon, Goodreads
Languages: English

CATEGORIES

- **Fiction:** Most fiction considered
- **Nonfiction:** Yes, Biography, Cookbooks, Crafting, Investing, Memoirs, Personal Finance
- **Excluded:** Erotica, Fantasy, Science Fiction, Vampires, Witches, Zombies

From the reviewer: I am an adult who has been reading since I was six. I love to discover debut authors who care about their books, which includes grammar and presentation. I hate reading books that look like they were just put together at the last minute.

Booksie's Blog (B9-046)

http://booksiesblog.blogspot.com
Sandie Kirkland | skirkland@triad.rr.com

eBooks	Audiobooks	Fees/Services	Tours
Kindle		No	No

Approximate turnaround time: Inquire
Where reviews are posted: Amazon, Goodreads
Languages: English

CATEGORIES

- **Fiction:** Most fiction considered
- **Nonfiction:** Yes, Biography, History, Science, Travel, True Crime
- **Excluded:** Christian, Economics, Erotica, Military Fiction, WWII-Related

From the reviewer: I've always been a huge reader. In fact, my husband's nickname for me is Booksie, and that's my car vanity plate as well! I prefer printed books. I have around seven-thousand books in my library and it may take me a while to get to your book, but I read and review everything I accept.

Bookwyrming Thoughts (B9-047)

Http://www.bookwyrmingthoughts.com

Sophia, Lupe, Anelise, and Ella | http://tinyurl.com/yad7uz2v

eBooks	Audiobooks	Fees/Services	Tours
Any	Yes	No	Yes

Approximate turnaround time: ~mo
Where reviews are posted: Amazon (by request); Goodreads, +Social
Languages: English

CATEGORIES

- **Fiction:** Most fiction considered
- **Nonfiction:** No
- **Excluded:** Children's, Erotica, Non-Fiction, Religious

From the reviewer: Bookwyrming Thoughts originally started with Sophia and expanded to a group blog in late 2014. We're a diverse group of four who enjoy reading, sharing our thoughts/opinions with other readers, and fangirling over the books we have a passion for. More additional details about each reviewer can be found on our "About" page.

Bound 4 Escape (B9-048)

http://www.bound4escape.com

Dawn Heslin | https://bound4escape.com/review-policies/

eBooks	Audiobooks	Fees/Services	Tours
No	Yes	Inquire	Yes

Approximate turnaround time: 2-3 mo
Where reviews are posted: Amazon, Goodreads, +Social
Languages: English

CATEGORIES

- **Fiction:** Most fiction considered
- **Nonfiction:** Yes
- **Excluded:** Erotica, Self-Help

From the reviewer: I own an online bookstore and I love to read most genres. I also like to listen to audiobooks while I'm working.

BOOK BLOGGERS

Brooke Blogs (B9-049)

http://www.brookeblogs.com
Brooke Bumgardner | http://tinyurl.com/yawr8q53

eBooks	Audiobooks	Fees/Services	Tours
Kindle	Yes	Yes	Yes

Approximate turnaround time: 2 mo
Where reviews are posted: Amazon, Goodreads, Kobo, BN
Languages: English

CATEGORIES

- **Fiction:** Contemporary Romance, Cozy Mystery, Fantasy, Historical Romance, Mystery, Science Fiction, Suspense, Thriller, YA
- **Nonfiction:** Yes, Cookbooks, Crafting, Health
- **Excluded:** Biography, Erotica, Horror

From the reviewer: I'm a 30-something mom of 2 children, living in eastern Ohio with my boyfriend. I work as the teen & children's program specialist at my local public library and I also have a virtual/author assistant business. I love sharing posts promoting books, whether through reviews or spotlights/interviews/guest posts and I am happy to share giveaways as well.

By the Book (B9-051)

http://rbclibrary.wordpress.com
Beckie Burnham | msudawgtoo@comsouth.net

eBooks	Audiobooks	Fees/Services	Tours
Kindle		No	No

Approximate turnaround time: 2-4 mo
Where reviews are posted: Amazon, Goodreads, +Social
Languages: English

CATEGORIES

- **Fiction:** Christian Fiction
- **Nonfiction:** Yes, Cookbooks, Devotionals, Memoirs
- **Excluded:** Erotica, LGBTQ, Self-Help

From the reviewer: I am a self-acknowledged crazy book lady who loves to get others reading great fiction. I review Christian fiction almost exclusively, but will consider nonfiction or "clean reads".

Caitlyn Lynch, Author (B9-052)

http://www.caitlynlynch.com

Caitlyn | http://www.caitlynlynch.com/book-review-policy

eBooks	Audiobooks	Fees/Services	Tours
Kindle	No	No	No

Approximate turnaround time: Inquire
Where reviews are posted: Amazon, Goodreads, +Social
Languages: English

CATEGORIES

- **Fiction:** Erotica, Romance
- **Nonfiction:** Yes, Cover Design, Self-Publishing, Writing
- **Excluded:** Christian, Horror, Inspirational

From the reviewer: I am an Australian author and mother of two who loves to read romance as much as I love to write it!

Carly's Cozy Corner (B9-053)

http://www.carlyscozycorner.blogspot.com

Carmen | http://tinyurl.com/y8darwqr

eBooks	Audiobooks	Fees/Services	Tours
Kindle, EPUB		No	No

Approximate turnaround time: 1-2 mo
Where reviews are posted: Amazon, Goodreads, BN, +Social
Languages: English, Spanish

CATEGORIES

- **Fiction:** Contemporary Romance, Dystopian, Historical Romance, Horror, Mystery, NA, Paranormal, Paranormal Romance, Science Fiction, Thriller, Urban Fantasy, YA
- **Nonfiction:** No
- **Excluded:** Erotica

From the reviewer: I am a mother of two who enjoys reading all sorts of books. My favorite genres to read are mystery, romance, and YA.

BOOK BLOGGERS

Cat Chat with Caren and Cody (B9-055)

http://www.catchatwithcarenandcody.com
Caren Gittleman | cgittleman@mi.rr.com

eBooks	Audiobooks	Fees/Services	Tours
No		Yes	No

Approximate turnaround time: 4-6 wk
Where reviews are posted: Social
Languages: English

CATEGORIES

- **Fiction:** Cat-Related
- **Nonfiction:** Yes, Cats
- **Excluded:** Anything unrelated to cats

From the reviewer: I am an experienced digital influencer. My book reviews are in high demand. I have been reviewing books on my blogs for over 6 years now.

Charlotte the Book Sniffer (B9-056)

https://charlottethebooksniffer.blogspot.co.uk/
Charlotte | charlottethebooksniffer@gmail.com

eBooks	Audiobooks	Fees/Services	Tours
Kindle, PDF		No	Yes

Approximate turnaround time: 1 wk-1 mo
Where reviews are posted: Amazon, Goodreads
Languages: English

CATEGORIES

- **Fiction:** Contemporary, Dystopian, Fantasy, Middle Grade, NA, Romance, Thriller, YA
- **Nonfiction:** No
- **Excluded:** Biography, Erotica, Graphic, Horror

From the reviewer: I am a British student who is in love with books and the world of literature! I will review all books honestly and am happy to promote the author and novel in any way they wish!

Cheryl Currie (B9-232)

http://www.cherylcurrie.com/e-book-reviews
Cheryl Currie | http://tinyurl.com/yb67nxp7

eBooks	Audiobooks	Fees/Services	Tours
Kindle, Mobi, EPUB, PDF	Yes	No	No

Approximate turnaround time: Inquire
Where reviews are posted: Amazon, Goodreads, + Social
Languages: English

CATEGORIES

- **Fiction:** Most fiction considered
- **Nonfiction:** Yes, Marketing, Publishing, Writing
- **Excluded:** Erotica

From the reviewer: I'm a published writer who balances writing with reading. I recently added book reviews to my established website for new authors who often have limited funds to gain exposure and obtain reviews. My offer includes advice on how to find a readership for your novel.

Cindy's Love of Books (B9-057)

http://cindysloveofbooks.com
Cindy | http://cindysloveofbooks.com/contact-me

eBooks	Audiobooks	Fees/Services	Tours
Kindle	Yes	Yes	Yes

Approximate turnaround time: Inquire
Where reviews are posted: Social
Languages: English

CATEGORIES

- **Fiction:** Chick Lit, Children's, Contemporary, Dystopian, Fiction-General, Middle Grade, Mystery, Paranormal, Romance, Thriller, YA
- **Nonfiction:** No
- **Excluded:** Biography, Erotica, History, Horror, Nonfiction, Science Fiction, Self-Help

From the reviewer: Avid reader, stay at home mom who loves to read all kinds of books. My taste in genres is all over the place. If I'm not home reading, I am usually at a hockey arena. I prefer printed copy but will accept e-books. I love talking with authors and hosting tours, excerpts and giveaways.

GIVE updates: http://breve.link/e9give   GET updates: http://breve.link/e9get

Cookbook Papers (B9-058)

http://cookbookpapers.blogspot.com
Renee Shelton | sandandsuccotash@gmail.com

eBooks	Audiobooks	Fees/Services	Tours
Mobi, EPUB, PDF		Inquire	Yes

Approximate turnaround time: 2-6 wk
Where reviews are posted: Amazon, Goodreads, Smashwords, LibraryThing, BN, +Social
Languages: English

CATEGORIES

- **Fiction:** Cooking or Food Related
- **Nonfiction:** Yes, Cooking or Food Related (only)
- **Excluded:** Books without a strong theme of cooking or food; fiction must have recipies.

From the reviewer: I have a background in cooking and am a graduate from culinary school. My personal library contains over 800 cookbooks. I enjoy reading cookbooks and testing recipes, and work as a food stylist as part of my everyday job duty. Specialized cookbooks, food dictionaries, and cooking handbooks are welcome as those are the ones I get the most email feedback from readers. I work with both self-published authors publishing their own cookbooks, and with established publishing houses. I collect vintage and archival baking books as a hobby.

Crandom (B9-060)

http://www.crandomblog.com
Sandra | sandra@crandomblog.com

eBooks	Audiobooks	Fees/Services	Tours
Yes		Donations	Yes

Approximate turnaround time: 1-2 mo
Where reviews are posted: Amazon, Goodreads, Paperback Reviewer, LibraryThing, +Social
Languages: English

CATEGORIES

- **Fiction:** Most fiction considered
- **Nonfiction:** Yes
- **Excluded:** Erotica, Science Fiction

From the reviewer: I am a stay-at-home mom who reads in what little free time she has. I do it in order to help amazing authors get their work out there; word-of-mouth is awesome.

Create With Joy (B9-062)

http://www.create-with-joy.com
Ramona | createwithjoy@gmail.com

eBooks	Audiobooks	Fees/Services	Tours
Kindle, PDF		Inquire	Yes

Approximate turnaround time: Inquire
Where reviews are posted: Amazon, Goodreads, +Social
Languages: English

CATEGORIES

- **Fiction:** Children's, Cozy Mystery, Dystopian, Historical Fiction, Literary Fiction, Mystery, Poetry, Science Fiction, Suspense, Thriller, YA
- **Nonfiction:** Yes, Animals, Christian, Cookbooks, Cookbooks, Devotionals, Health, Inspirational, Memoirs, Nutrition, Pets, Self-Help, Wellness
- **Excluded:** Erotica, LGBTQ, Occult, Supernatural

From the reviewer: I am an inspirational writer, influential book reviewer, and book launch team member who is fascinated by the power of the written word! I'm passionate about reading, and welcome the opportunity to share your books and giveaways with my audience! I am the founder of The Book Nook, a community for book lovers at Create with Joy.

BOOK BLOGGERS

Crystal's Many Reviewers (B9-063)

http://www.crystalsmanyreviewers.com
None; use form | crystalsmanyreviewers@gmail.com

eBooks	Audiobooks	Fees/Services	Tours
Kindle, Nook		Yes	Yes

Approximate turnaround time: 12-16 wk
Where reviews are posted: Amazon, Goodreads, BN, +Social
Languages: English

CATEGORIES
- **Fiction:** Most fiction considered
- **Nonfiction:** Inquire
- **Excluded:** None specified

From the reviewer: Crystal's Many Reviewers is a blog that currently has 12 reviewers who enjoy reading a variety of different genres. We strive to provide completely HONEST reviews and we enjoy discovering new authors in our reading adventures!

Cultivate to Plate (B9-064)

http://www.cultivatetoplate.com
Renee Shelton | sandandsuccotash@gmail.com

eBooks	Audiobooks	Fees/Services	Tours
Mobi, EPUB, PDF		No	Yes

Approximate turnaround time: 2-6 wk
Where reviews are posted: Amazon, Goodreads, Smashwords, LibraryThing, BN, +Social
Languages: English

CATEGORIES

- **Fiction:** None
- **Nonfiction:** Yes, Gardening, Horticulture, Landscaping
- **Excluded:** Anything unrelated to gardening

From the reviewer: I live in Southern California, and practice organic gardening. I grow much of the vegetables my family eats, have a generous herb garden with herbs and edible flowers, have over 60 different fruit and nut trees, and grow several different berries. I preserve much of what we grow during the harvest season to enjoy for the rest of the year. While I do have ornamentals, I tend to plant what I can eat somehow since water is so precious. Cultivate to Plate blog is growing what I plant, and cooking with the harvest. I enjoy reading and sharing garden books for the blog.

Dab of Darkness (B9-065)

http://dabofdarkness.com/
Susan Voss | http://dabofdarkness.com/About/

eBooks	Audiobooks	Fees/Services	Tours
No	Yes	No	Yes

Approximate turnaround time: 1-4 mo
Where reviews are posted: Amazon, Goodreads, Audible, BookLikes, LibraryThing, +Social
Languages: English

CATEGORIES

- **Fiction:** Erotica, Fantasy, Historical Fiction, Mystery, Science Fiction, Thriller
- **Nonfiction:** Yes, Cookbooks, Crafting, History, Memoirs, Science
- **Excluded:** Contemporary Romance

From the reviewer: I'm a weaver and have many hours a day for audiobook listening pleasure. I love to cook. I'm a biologist by degree and live on a small farm with goats, donkeys, cats, chickens, and dogs.

Dakota's Den (B9-067)

http://www.dakotasden.net
Caren Gittleman | cgittleman@mi.rr.com

eBooks	Audiobooks	Fees/Services	Tours
No		Yes	No

Approximate turnaround time: 4-6 wk
Where reviews are posted: Social
Languages: English

CATEGORIES

- **Fiction:** Dog-related
- **Nonfiction:** Yes, Dog-related
- **Excluded:** Anything unrelated to dogs

From the reviewer: I am an experienced digital influencer. My book reviews are in high demand. I have been reviewing books on my blogs for over 6 years now.

Dark Matters (B9-068)

http://www.darkmattersblog.com
John Matsui | reviews@darkmattersblog.com

eBooks	Audiobooks	Fees/Services	Tours
Kindle	Yes	No	No

Approximate turnaround time: 2 mo
Where reviews are posted: Amazon, Goodreads, Reader's Favorite, +Social
Languages: English

CATEGORIES

- **Fiction:** Historical Fiction, Horror, Mystery, Paranormal, Science Fiction, Thriller
- **Nonfiction:** Yes, Business-only
- **Excluded:** Erotica, Fantasy, Romance

From the reviewer: I was a journalist for twenty-five years and the editor of a section that included the book pages. I wrote a book review column for five years. I've written and self-published two thrillers and four thriller film scripts.

DarWrites (B9-069)

https://darwrites.wordpress.com/dar-writes-4/blog
Darlene Reilley | https://darwrites.wordpress.com/contact-me

eBooks	Audiobooks	Fees/Services	Tours
Kindle	No	No	Yes

Approximate turnaround time: 1-2 mo
Where reviews are posted: Amazon, Goodreads, +Social
Languages: English

CATEGORIES

- **Fiction:** Dystopian, Literary Fiction, Paranormal, Romance, Science Fiction
- **Nonfiction:** Yes, Anthropology, Cookbooks, Crafting, History, Military, Science
- **Excluded:** Biography, Devotionals, Erotica, Memoirs

From the reviewer: I am a book dragon who loves to settle in with tea and the best novels. I completed my MFA and am writing my novels and working as a freelance writer. I will give an honest review.

BOOK BLOGGERS

Dedicated Readers (B9-071)

http://dedicatedreaders.blogspot.com/
Esther | http://dedicatedreaders.blogspot.com/p/r.html

eBooks	Audiobooks	Fees/Services	Tours
Yes		No	No

Approximate turnaround time: 2 wk
Where reviews are posted: Goodreads, +Social
Languages: English

CATEGORIES

- **Fiction:** Erotica, Romance-All Genres
- **Nonfiction:** Yes, Cookbooks
- **Excluded:** Christian, Comics, Dystopian

From the reviewer: I just love reading. That's it.

Diana's Book Reviews (B9-072)

http://dianasbookreviews.com/
Diana | http://dianasbookreviews.com/book-review-policy/

eBooks	Audiobooks	Fees/Services	Tours
Kindle, PDF	Yes	No	Yes

Approximate turnaround time: 1-2 mo
Where reviews are posted: Amazon, Goodreads, +Social
Languages: English

CATEGORIES

- **Fiction:** Chick Lit, Children's, Christian Romance, Historical Fiction, Mystery, Paranormal, Romance, Women's Fiction, YA
- **Nonfiction:** Yes, Crafting, Devotionals, Memoirs
- **Excluded:** Dystopian, Erotica, Horror, LGBTQ, Science Fiction

From the reviewer: I am a middle-aged woman who loves to read. I love to read woman's fiction, clean romance, and historical fiction. I would be happy to do a Rafflecopter to give out an e-book and to promote your work.

Donovan's Literary Services (B9-074)

http://donovansliteraryservices.com
Diane Donovan, Editor | donovan@sonic.net

eBooks	**Audiobooks**	**Fees/Services**	**Tours**
Kindle, PDF		Yes	No

Approximate turnaround time: 2 mo
Where reviews are posted: Inquire
Languages: English

CATEGORIES
- **Fiction:** Most fiction considered
- **Nonfiction:** Yes
- **Excluded:** Inquire

From the reviewer: I have been reviewing books for over thirty years. I am a generalist, which means I read and enjoy a wide range of genres, from young adult fiction and picture book fiction to science fiction (I especially enjoy hard science stories) and nonfiction. Each month I select a certain number of books from well-written queries and invite authors to send them for review.

BOOK BLOGGERS

Doodles, Doodles Everywhere (B9-075)

http://gopaintbrush.blogspot.com
Aparna Singh | doodlesdoodleseverywhere@gmail.com

eBooks	Audiobooks	Fees/Services	Tours
Kindle		Yes	Yes

Approximate turnaround time: 2 mo
Where reviews are posted: Amazon, Goodreads, +Social
Languages: English

CATEGORIES

- **Fiction:** Chick Lit, Contemporary, Dystopian, Fantasy, Graphic novels, Horror, Manga, Paranormal, Romance, Science Fiction, Thriller
- **Nonfiction:** Yes, Architecture, Arts, Crafting, DIY, Photography, Technology, Travel
- **Excluded:** Autobiography, Biography, Children's, Crime, Erotica, Historical Fiction, Memoirs, Mysteries, Religious

From the reviewer: I'm Aparna Singh, just another nerdy book blogger from New Delhi, with a love for design, photography and fashion. Oh, and I also happen to be an architect. I prefer to read for my own enjoyment and love to share my views on what I read. My review style is subject to change but what you can usually count on is that my reviews are mostly very subjective and also honest. I believe in constructive criticism, stating my opinions whether positive or negative, without being rude or demeaning to anyone. I absolutely love getting to know new authors and finding out more books to read.

Dreams Come Through Reading (B9-076)

http://dcttr.blogspot.com

Chelsea | http://tinyurl.com/ych3kc87

eBooks	Audiobooks	Fees/Services	Tours
Mobi, PDF		No	No

Approximate turnaround time: 1-2 mo

Where reviews are posted: Amazon, Goodreads, +Social

Languages: English

CATEGORIES

- **Fiction:** Dystopian, Fantasy, Historical Fiction, Middle Grade, NA, Paranormal, Romance, Science Fiction, YA
- **Nonfiction:** No
- **Excluded:** Comics, Erotica, Manga, Nonfiction

From the reviewer: We are both college students, who love to read a multitude of books. I might not currently be with any tours, but I will do promotional things like interviews, guest posts, or other if you would like.

BOOK BLOGGERS

Electively Paige (B9-233)

http://electivelypaige.com

Paige Boggs | http://electivelypaige.com/book-review-policy/

eBooks	Audiobooks	Fees/Services	Tours
Kindle, Mobi	Yes	Yes	Yes

Approximate turnaround time: Inquire

Where reviews are posted: Amazon, Goodreads, BN, + Social, on request

Languages: English

CATEGORIES

- **Fiction:** Chick Lit, Christian Fiction, Contemporary Romance, Fantasy, Fiction-General, Historical Fiction, Historical Romance, Literary Fiction, Mystery, Science Fiction, Suspense, Thriller, Zombies
- **Nonfiction:** Yes, Adventure, Christian, History, Memoirs
- **Excluded:** Children's

From the reviewer: I'm a nerdy, animal-loving, wanderlust-filled hiker and hardcore bookworm, who started my blog because shouting from the rooftops about everything I love in the aforementioned categories was getting old-(and is apparently frowned upon(who knew?). For that thing called work you have to do to keep the furkids in kibble I work alongside amazing authors and publishers to help bring attention to their books through marketing and publicity tactics such as blog tours, online release parties, newsletter building efforts, and more. I totally believe I'd survive the zombie apocalypse, so long as I don't get cornered saving a squirrel or something.

Ellie Is Uhm ... A Bookworm (B9-234)

http://www.ellieisuhmabookworm.com
J Elise Ortiz | earth2mother@gmail.com

eBooks	Audiobooks	Fees/Services	Tours
Kindle, Mobi, EPUB, PDF	Yes	No	Yes

Approximate turnaround time: Inquire
Where reviews are posted: Amazon, Goodreads
Languages: English

CATEGORIES

- **Fiction:** Contemporary Romance, Erotica, NA, Romantic Comedy, Romantic Suspense, YA
- **Nonfiction:** No
- **Excluded:** Biography

From the reviewer: I discovered my love for ALL things books while a senior in high school, when a trip to the library for research on a term paper brought me (mistakenly) to the literature section. While there, two books—Gone With the Wind by Margaret Mitchell and A Knight in Shining Armor by Jude Deveraux—grabbed my attention. Needless to say the term paper took a back seat...

Since then, I have been reading non-stop—whenever and wherever I am (job be damned! lol). I'm just your an average 40-something yr old female with lots of a time on her hands, when my puppy baby lets me rest that is, as I am unmarried with no children.

With the introduction of e-books, I have abandoned my love of libraries (since I have not physically stepped inside one for 5+ years!), but vows to go (one day) in the near future & start visiting again regularly! It's on the Bucket List!

I enjoy hearing from fellow book lovers, whether its a book recommendation, an opinion on a book genre/theme, or just a debate/discussion about a book's outcome. I'm open to receiving email correspondence and will answer any/all questions.

If you'd like to reach out for a book recommendation, to get feedback from a book review, or to just shoot the breeze, contact me at earth2mother@gmail.com.

Emeraldfire's Bookmark (B9-077)

http://rubyandthetwins.blogspot.com
Mareena McGirr | emeraldfiresbookmark@mail.com

eBooks	Audiobooks	Fees/Services	Tours
Mobi, EPUB, PDF, iBooks		No	No

Approximate turnaround time: 10-14 days
Where reviews are posted: Amazon, Goodreads, +Social
Languages: English

CATEGORIES

- **Fiction:** Christian Fiction, Contemporary, Fantasy, Historical Fiction, Historical Romance, Horror, Mystery, Paranormal Romance, Science Fiction, Suspense, Thriller, Vampires, YA
- **Nonfiction:** Yes, Autobiography, Biography, History, Memoirs, True Crime
- **Excluded:** BDSM, Cookbooks, How-To, M/M, Zombies

From the reviewer: I was born in Belfast, Northern Ireland, but moved to America when I was 5. My parents owned two Irish restaurants—one in Albany, New York the other in Dennisport, Cape Cod. I host an Irish radio program with my mom in upstate New York called 'Proud to be Irish'. I'm an avid reader, love history (mainly Irish history), writing, music, and arts and crafts. I also love to laugh and meet new people. I am cheerfully owned by three adorable eight year old rescue cats named Ruby, Leila and Lollipop.

Empty Mirror Magazine (B9-078)

http://www.emptymirrorbooks.com
Denise | http://www.emptymirrorbooks.com/get-in-touch

eBooks	Audiobooks	Fees/Services	Tours
No		Yes	No

Approximate turnaround time: 2-12 wk
Where reviews are posted: Social
Languages: English

CATEGORIES

- **Fiction:** Poetry
- **Nonfiction:** Yes, 1960s, Arts, Avant-Garde, Beat Generation, Biography, Literary Criticism, Poetry, Surrealism
- **Excluded:** Fiction

From the reviewer: I'm the editor of a long-established online literary magazine; I love learning about art, literature, and the people who create them. I love turning others onto good books and authors.

English Teacher's Corner (B9-079)

http://englishteacherscorner.com
Mateusz | http://englishteacherscorner.com/contact-me

eBooks	Audiobooks	Fees/Services	Tours
PDF		Yes	No

Approximate turnaround time: 2 mo
Where reviews are posted: Amazon, +Social
Languages: English

CATEGORIES

- **Fiction:** Children's
- **Nonfiction:** Yes, Educational, English, Teaching
- **Excluded:** All except those noted

From the reviewer: My name's Mateusz Wawrzynowicz. I've been working as an ESL teacher for seven years now. I received my BA in English and my MA in Sociolinguistics from Adam Mickiewicz University.

BOOK BLOGGERS

Epic Book Quest (B9-080)

http://epicbookquest.com
Johanna | http://tinyurl.com/ybsxzvov

eBooks	Audiobooks	Fees/Services	Tours
No		Inquire	No

Approximate turnaround time: 1-2 mo
Where reviews are posted: Amazon, Goodreads, BN, Bookstr, +Social
Languages: English

CATEGORIES

- **Fiction:** Most fiction considered
- **Nonfiction:** Yes, Cookbooks, Devotionals, Dog Training, Gardening, Memoirs, Self-Help
- **Excluded:** Anti/non-Christian Religious, Astrology, Erotica, Fantasy, Horror, New Age, Paranormal, Poetry, Science Fiction, Werewolf, Zombies

From the reviewer: Avid reader and lover of all things literary! I love non-fiction and cozy mysteries, and if you want to send me a print copy I will gladly post a review, or host a giveaway and promote your page. Just ask!

Fallxnrobin (B9-082)

https://fallxnrobins.wordpress.com
Zoe | https://fallxnrobins.wordpress.com/review-policy

eBooks	Audiobooks	Fees/Services	Tours
Mobi		No	Yes

Approximate turnaround time: 1 mo
Where reviews are posted: Goodreads, +Social
Languages: English

CATEGORIES

- **Fiction:** Dystopian, Fantasy, Horror, Mystery, Science Fiction, Thriller
- **Nonfiction:** No
- **Excluded:** Erotica, Nonfiction

From the reviewer: Just another teenage girl who loves reading. I'm always reading something, it's just a matter of whether it's a book or a fantic. I particularly enjoy science fiction and fantasy but I'm always up for trying books that are out of my comfort zone!

Fangirls Read it First (B9-083)

https://fangirlsreaditfirst.wordpress.com
Brit, Amanda, Vanessa, Tammy and Greta
http://tinyurl.com/y8wlan98

eBooks	Audiobooks	Fees/Services	Tours
EPUB, PDF		No	Yes

Approximate turnaround time: few wk
Where reviews are posted: Amazon, Goodreads
Languages: English

CATEGORIES

- **Fiction:** Most fiction considered
- **Nonfiction:** Yes, Biography, Coloring Books, Memoirs
- **Excluded:** Inquire

From the reviewer: We are a book club full of people that love to review new things!

Feathered Quill Book Reviews (B9-084)

http://www.featheredquill.com
Ellen Feld | info@featheredquill.com

eBooks	Audiobooks	Fees/Services	Tours
Inquire		Yes	No

Approximate turnaround time: 2-4 wk
Where reviews are posted: BN, Google Play Books, Book-Critique, Book-Views, +Social
Languages: English

CATEGORIES

- **Fiction:** Children's, Fantasy, Fiction-General, Historical Fiction, Humor, Mystery, Poetry, Romance, Science Fiction, Short Stories, Suspense, YA
- **Nonfiction:** Yes, Animals, Biography, Business, Cookbooks, History, How-To, Inspirational, Memoirs, Parenting, Pets, Sports, Travel
- **Excluded:** Erotica

From the reviewer: Feathered Quill also hosts the annual Feathered Quill Book Awards to bring awareness to indie authors across a broad range of genres. It was named one of the best award programs for independent authors by The Association of Independent Authors! For more information, please visit our website.

BOOK BLOGGERS

Fic Gal (B9-085)

http://www.ficgal.com/book-club
Barbara Desmond | weirdmuser@gmail.com

eBooks	Audiobooks	Fees/Services	Tours
Kindle, EPUB		Inquire	Yes

Approximate turnaround time: Inquire
Where reviews are posted: Amazon, Goodreads, +Social
Languages: English

CATEGORIES

- **Fiction:** Fantasy, Horror, Mystery, Paranormal, Thriller, Witches
- **Nonfiction:** No
- **Excluded:** Erotica, Memoirs, Nonfiction, Poetry, Romance

From the reviewer: I love to read. I even read when I'm walking. I love books, especially witchy books.

Firstbooklove (B9-235)

http://firstbooklove.wordpress.com
Michelle Yeo | yeomichelle_2244@hotmail.com

eBooks	Audiobooks	Fees/Services	Tours
Kindle, Mobi, EPUB, PDF	Yes	No	Yes

Approximate turnaround time: Inquire
Where reviews are posted: Goodreads
Languages: English

CATEGORIES

- **Fiction:** Contemporary, Dystopian, Fantasy, Paranormal, Romance, Science Fiction
- **Nonfiction:** No
- **Excluded:** Erotica

From the reviewer: I'm a 21 year old bookstagrammer and book blogger! I enjoy reading books as they often quieten my mind and yet they make me think so much! Hope that I will be able to grow my blog over the years!

For the Love of Books (B9-087)

http://mommiebethers.blogspot.com/
Beth Milinski | Mommiebethers@gmail.com

eBooks	Audiobooks	Fees/Services	Tours
PDF		Yes	No

Approximate turnaround time: 3-4 mo
Where reviews are posted: Amazon, Goodreads, +Social
Languages: English

CATEGORIES

- **Fiction:** Christian Fiction, Clean Romance, Mystery
- **Nonfiction:** Yes, Biography, Legal, Memoirs, Medical, Writing
- **Excluded:** Comics, Dystopian, Erotica, Horror

From the reviewer: I am a stay-at-home who is disabled. I love to read and review books, especially all types of Christian Fiction, historical fiction, mystery, clean romance, legal, medical, and general fiction. I love finding new authors and reading debut novels.

Fortified by Books (B9-088)

https://fortifiedbybooks.com
Rachelle | http://tinyurl.com/ydd8p8rh

eBooks	Audiobooks	Fees/Services	Tours
Kindle		No	No

Approximate turnaround time: Depends on Release date
Where reviews are posted: Amazon, Goodreads, +Social
Languages: English

CATEGORIES

- **Fiction:** Children's, Contemporary, Dystopian, Fantasy, Historical Fiction, Science Fiction, YA
- **Nonfiction:** Yes, History, Memoirs
- **Excluded:** Erotica, Inspirational Fiction, Paranormal Romance, Religious

From the reviewer: I'm a recent college graduate, with dreams of going to grad school for Library Science and Information Technology. Tolkien is in my blood and I'm a hobbit at heart.

From Me to You (B9-089)

http://frommetoyouvideophoto.blogspot.com
Jess F. | https://fromjesstoyouservices.wordpress.com/contact/

eBooks	Audiobooks	Fees/Services	Tours
Kindle, Mobi		Yes	Yes

Approximate turnaround time: Inquire
Where reviews are posted: Amazon, Goodreads, BN, Kobo, LibraryThing, +Social
Languages: English

CATEGORIES
- **Fiction:** Children's, Entertainment, Erotica, Fantasy, Fiction-General, Historical Fiction, Paranormal, Romance, Science Fiction, YA
- **Nonfiction:** No
- **Excluded:** Horror

From the reviewer: Details are on my website.

Fur Everywhere (B9-091)

http://fureverywhere.blogspot.com
Sierra | fureverywhere@gmail.com

eBooks	Audiobooks	Fees/Services	Tours
No		Yes	Yes

Approximate turnaround time: 1-2 mo
Where reviews are posted: Amazon, Goodreads, +Social
Languages: English

CATEGORIES
- **Fiction:** Cat-Related
- **Nonfiction:** Yes, Cats
- **Excluded:** Comics, Dystopian, Erotica, Fantasy, Horror, Science Fiction

From the reviewer: I am a professional blogger who blogs about cats. I am passionate about helping cats and cat parents. I love to read and enjoy reviewing books.

Geo Librarian (B9-093)

http://geolibrarian.blogspot.com

Heidi | hg195@yahoo.com

eBooks	Audiobooks	Fees/Services	Tours
Kindle		No	Yes

Approximate turnaround time: 2-4 mo

Where reviews are posted: Amazon, Goodreads, +Social

Languages: English

CATEGORIES

- **Fiction:** Children's, Geography, Middle Grade
- **Nonfiction:** Yes, Children's, Middle Grade
- **Excluded:** Erotica, Fiction-General

From the reviewer: I am an elementary school librarian who loves to read and talk about children's literature.

Get Kids to Read (B9-094)

http://www.getkidstoread.co

Patrick Tierney | patrick@getkidstoread.co

eBooks	Audiobooks	Fees/Services	Tours
Kindle		Yes	Yes

Approximate turnaround time: 1-2 mo

Where reviews are posted: Amazon, Goodreads, +Social

Languages: English

CATEGORIES

- **Fiction:** Adventure, Children's, Fantasy, Middle Grade, Mystery, Science Fiction, YA
- **Nonfiction:** No
- **Excluded:** Christian Fiction, Erotica, Romance

From the reviewer: I have been a reviewer for four years because I love getting the right book into every child's hand.

BOOK BLOGGERS

Hall Ways Blog (B9-095)

http://kristinehallways.blogspot.com
Kristine Hall | Use website contact form

eBooks	Audiobooks	Fees/Services	Tours
Any	Yes	Yes	Yes

Approximate turnaround time: Inquire
Where reviews are posted: Amazon, Goodreads, +Social
Languages: English

CATEGORIES

- **Fiction:** Adventure, Children's, Fantasy, Fiction-General, Historical Fiction, Horror, Humor, Literary Fiction, Middle Grade, Mystery, Paranormal, Science Fiction, YA
- **Nonfiction:** Yes
- **Excluded:** Cookbooks, Crafting, Erotica, NA, Romance

From the reviewer: I am a professional reviewer for numerous publicity services, authors and publishers. I have a bachelor's in modern languages, a master's in library science, am a certified teacher and librarian, and a proud member of a Grammar Police.

Harder to Destroy (B9-096)

http://hardertodestroy.com/category/book-reviews
Joe | josephjmolloy@gmail.com

eBooks	Audiobooks	Fees/Services	Tours
Kindle		No	No

Approximate turnaround time: Inquire
Where reviews are posted: Amazon, Goodreads, +Social
Languages: English

CATEGORIES

- **Fiction:** None
- **Nonfiction:** Yes, Biography, History, Martial Arts, Philosophy, Science
- **Excluded:** Erotica, Fiction

From the reviewer: I use my reviewing to learn more from the books I read.

Her Book Thoughts (B9-097)

http://herbookthoughts.reads-it.com

Paula | http://herbookthoughts.reads-it.com/?page_id=120

eBooks	Audiobooks	Fees/Services	Tours
Kindle, EPUB		Yes	Yes

Approximate turnaround time: 1 mo
Where reviews are posted: Amazon, Goodreads
Languages: English

CATEGORIES

- **Fiction:** Contemporary Romance, Fantasy, Middle Grade, NA, Paranormal, YA
- **Nonfiction:** Yes, Memoirs, Self-Help
- **Excluded:** Erotica

From the reviewer: Hey guys! I'm Paula! I'm twenty and a proud Filipina. Reading and book blogging makes me happy. I'm a love, movie, music, and people enthusiast! I love bookstores, coffee shops, and libraries. Make me a mixtape and we'll be friends forever!

Historical Fiction Obsession (B9-098)

http://www.historicalfictionobsession.blogspot.com.

Kim | kimbers10@yahoo.com

eBooks	Audiobooks	Fees/Services	Tours
Kindle, PDF		Inquire	Yes

Approximate turnaround time: 1-2 mo
Where reviews are posted: Amazon, Goodreads
Languages: English

CATEGORIES

- **Fiction:** Historical Fiction
- **Nonfiction:** Yes, Autobiography, Biography (historical), Memoirs
- **Excluded:** Christian, Comics, Erotica, Supernatural, YA

From the reviewer: I am an English and reading teacher, as well as a mother of 3-year old, identical twin boys. I absolutely love historical fiction, preferably pre-1800's, and dealing with kings and queens and their courts. I also enjoy reading novels set during the Civil War, but my favorite novels are definitely those set in medieval England, Scotland and France.

BOOK BLOGGERS

Home is Where the Wine Is (B9-099)

http://homeiswherethewineis.com
Amy | http://homeiswherethewineis.com/review-requests

eBooks	Audiobooks	Fees/Services	Tours
Mobi, EPUB, PDF		No	Yes

Approximate turnaround time: 1-2 mo
Where reviews are posted: Amazon, Goodreads, +Social
Languages: English

CATEGORIES

- **Fiction:** Contemporary Romance, Erotica, Humor, Paranormal, Romance, Thriller, YA
- **Nonfiction:** Yes, Wine
- **Excluded:** Biography, Cookbooks, Memoirs

From the reviewer: I have been blogging for over four years and have been an avid reader all my life. I love my relationships with my author friends. Feel free to contact me through Facebook if you wish to connect!

Hott Books (B9-100)

http://www.hottbooks.com
Gina Hott | http://www.hottbooks.com/about/

eBooks	Audiobooks	Fees/Services	Tours
Kindle		No	Yes

Approximate turnaround time: 2-6 mo
Where reviews are posted: Goodreads, +Social
Languages: English

CATEGORIES

- **Fiction:** Children's, Christian Romance, Contemporary Romance, Historical Romance, Middle Grade, Mystery, YA
- **Nonfiction:** No
- **Excluded:** Erotica, Horror, LGBTQ, Nonfiction, Politics

From the reviewer: I'm a married mother of three who spends my spare time either cheering at my kids various sporting events or reading. I read a bit of everything, including previewing books for her plethora of nieces and nephews.

I Create Purty Thangs (B9-101)

http://icreatepurtythangs.blogspot.com

Julie Baswell | jgbaswell@hotmail.com

eBooks	Audiobooks	Fees/Services	Tours
Kindle		Yes	Yes

Approximate turnaround time: 1-2 mo

Where reviews are posted: Amazon, Goodreads, BN, +Social

Languages: English

CATEGORIES

- **Fiction:** Detective, Historical Romance, Horror, Humor, Mystery, Paranormal
- **Nonfiction:** Yes, Cookbooks, Crafting, How-To
- **Excluded:** Biography, Erotica, Sports

From the reviewer: After blogging for over three years, I have spread my blog across the internet and am starting to reap the benefits of it. I have a steady increase of followers. My experience increases daily. I work every day on improving my blog content and following and further getting my name out to affiliates. I am honest, hardworking, and reputable. When I commit, I always come through on time. I am also very good at spelling and punctuation.

I Heart Reading (B9-236)

http://iheartreading.net
Majanka Verstraete | iheartreading.reviews@gmail.com

eBooks	Audiobooks	Fees/Services	Tours
No		Yes	Yes

Approximate turnaround time: Inquire
Where reviews are posted: Amazon, Goodreads, BN, + Social
Languages: English, Dutch

CATEGORIES

- **Fiction:** Children's, Fantasy, Ghost, Historical Fiction, Mystery, NA, Paranormal Mystery, Paranormal Romance, Thriller, YA
- **Nonfiction:** Yes, Marketing, Publishing, Self-Help, Spirituality
- **Excluded:** Inquire

From the reviewer: I'm 27 years old and live in Belgium. I have a Master of Law degree and am studying for a Master of Criminology degree. Reading is one of my greatest passions. I used to read mainly epic fantasy but now I read almost every genre, although ghost stories are my favorites.

I'm also an author. I write YA/NA paranormal and children's books.

Whatever spare time I have left, I spend binge-watching Netflix series and playing World of Warcraft.

I'm Shelf-ish (B9-103)

http://www.imshelfish.com
Tracee or Tim | http://www.imshelfish.com/p/contact-me.html

eBooks	Audiobooks	Fees/Services	Tours
Kindle		Yes	Yes

Approximate turnaround time: 2 mo
Where reviews are posted: Amazon, Goodreads, +Social
Languages: English

CATEGORIES

- **Fiction:** Horror, Mystery, Paranormal, Romance, Suspense, Thriller, YA
- **Nonfiction:** Yes, Cookbooks, Memoirs
- **Excluded:** Christian

From the reviewer: I am a mom of two who has been helping promote authors for the last 8 years. My life revolves not only around my family, but around our shared love of reading.

Icefairy's Treasure Chest (B9-102)

http://icefairystreasurechest.blogspot.com
Bing | icefairyisme@gmail.com

eBooks	Audiobooks	Fees/Services	Tours
Kindle, PDF		Yes	Yes

Approximate turnaround time: 4-6 wk
Where reviews are posted: Amazon, Goodreads
Languages: English

CATEGORIES

- **Fiction:** Children's, Family-Friendly, Mystery, Romance, Science Fiction, Suspense, Thriller, YA
- **Nonfiction:** Yes, Arts, Crafting, Fitness, Food, Health, Parenting
- **Excluded:** Erotica

From the reviewer: I am a mom with 3 kids in different age groups. I love to read and take every opportunity to nurture my kids' interest in reading. That's why I give priority to children's books when processing review requests. I prefer print copies to e-books, especially for picture books. I'm always open to hosting book or gift card giveaways to help promote a book.

Imi Reviews Books (B9-237)

https://imireviewsbooks.wordpress.com/
Imogen Gray | Imireviewsbooks@gmail.com

eBooks	Audiobooks	Fees/Services	Tours
Kindle, Mobi		No	Yes

Approximate turnaround time: Inquire
Where reviews are posted: Amazon, Goodreads, + Social
Languages: English

CATEGORIES

- **Fiction:** Contemporary, Fantasy, NA, Romance, Science Fiction, Thriller, YA
- **Nonfiction:** No
- **Excluded:** Erotica

From the reviewer: Writer at heart, reader in reality, Imi spends as much time as possible with her nose in a book. She adores fantasy and believes there is nothing better than being transported by words to another land/world/planet/universe.

Impression in Ink (B9-104)

http://impressionsinink.blogspot.com
Annette | bellevieanne@gmail.com

eBooks	Audiobooks	Fees/Services	Tours
Kindle		Yes	Yes

Approximate turnaround time: 1-2 mo
Where reviews are posted: Amazon, Goodreads, +Social
Languages: English

CATEGORIES

- **Fiction:** Christian Fiction, Classics, Detective, Fantasy, Historical Fiction, Mystery, Mythology, Poetry, YA
- **Nonfiction:** Yes, Behavioral Science, Biography, History, Holocaust, Memoirs, Military, Psychology, Reference Books, Travel
- **Excluded:** Comics, Erotica, Horror, Paranormal, Thrasher

From the reviewer: I've been blogging and writing reviews ten years. I'm an avid reader. My other interests are journal writing and art journaling.

Jbarrett5 Book Reviews (B9-105)

http://jbarrett5.blogspot.com
Julie Barrett | jbarrett5@cox.net

eBooks	Audiobooks	Fees/Services	Tours
Kindle, EPUB		No	Yes

Approximate turnaround time: few wks
Where reviews are posted: Amazon, Goodreads, BN, LibraryThing, Google Circles, BookLikes, +Social
Languages: English

CATEGORIES

- **Fiction:** Romance
- **Nonfiction:** Yes
- **Excluded:** Erotica, Fantasy, Horror, Religious, Science Fiction

From the reviewer: I knit and crochet for charity.

JC's Book Haven (B9-106)

http://jcbookhaven.blogspot.com

Jaclyn Canada, Melody and Matt | http://tinyurl.com/yctq3gfa

eBooks	Audiobooks	Fees/Services	Tours
Kindle		No	Yes

Approximate turnaround time: 1-2 mo
Where reviews are posted: Amazon, Goodreads, BN, +Social
Languages: English

CATEGORIES

- **Fiction:** Crime, Dystopian, Horror, Paranormal, Science Fiction, Thriller, Urban Fantasy, YA
- **Nonfiction:** No
- **Excluded:** Biography, Christian, Erotica, Nonfiction

From the reviewer: Hi, my name is Jaclyn. My genres of choice are paranormal, urban fantasy, and dystopian. I enjoy young adult and adult. I shy away from anything I know will make me cry. My quirks include walking into walls, hating repetitive noises, and smiling gleefully at my favorite words. Some of those words are marshmallow, ninja, shenanigans, and nemesis.

BOOK BLOGGERS

Jen's Corner Spot (B9-107)

http://www.jenscornerspot.blogspot.com
Jennifer Yarbrough | http://www.jenscornerspot.blogspot.com

eBooks	Audiobooks	Fees/Services	Tours
Kindle	Yes	No	Yes

Approximate turnaround time: 1-2 mo
Where reviews are posted: Amazon, Goodreads, +Social
Languages: English

CATEGORIES

- **Fiction:** BDSM, Contemporary Romance, Erotica, Fantasy, LGBTQ, Mystery, NA, Paranormal, Science Fiction, Thriller
- **Nonfiction:** No
- **Excluded:** Autobiography, Biography, Christian, Comics

From the reviewer: I am a wife and mother of two who LOVES to read and have a little private time to myself. I love most genres but am partial to Fantasy and Paranormal. I'm honest in my opinions and will tell it like I see it. I just read a little over 600 books and novellas this past year. I love how when I read it's like watching a movie. If you want to send me a print copy of your book I will happily run a raffle copter to give the book away and promote your page. Just ask me!!

Jersey Girl Book Reviews (B9-108)

http://jerseygirlbookreviews.blogspot.com/
Kathleen Anderson | jerseygirlbookreviews@yahoo.com

eBooks	Audiobooks	Fees/Services	Tours
Kindle, Mobi, PDF		No	Yes

Approximate turnaround time: 4-6 wk
Where reviews are posted: Amazon, Goodreads, BN, +Social
Languages: English

CATEGORIES

- **Fiction:** Chick Lit, Christian Fiction, Contemporary Romance, Mystery, Suspense, Thriller, Women's Fiction
- **Nonfiction:** Yes, Business, Cookbooks, Memoirs, Self-Help, True Crime
- **Excluded:** Children's, Erotica, Fantasy, Horror, Paranormal, Poetry, Science Fiction

From the reviewer: I am an avid bookworm who loves to share my passion for reading.

BOOK BLOGGERS

Jersey Girl Sizzling Book Reviews (B9-109)

http://jerseygirlsizzlingbookreviews.blogspot.com
Kathleen Anderson | jerseygirlbookreviews@yahoo.com

eBooks	Audiobooks	Fees/Services	Tours
Kindle, Mobi, PDF		No	Yes

Approximate turnaround time: 4-6 wk
Where reviews are posted: Amazon, Goodreads, BN, +Social
Languages: English

CATEGORIES

- **Fiction:** Erotica, Romance
- **Nonfiction:** No
- **Excluded:** All except those noted

From the reviewer: I am an avid bookworm who loves to share my passion for reading.

Just One More Chapter (B9-110)

http://www.justonemorechapter.net
Annie | I.heart.books.831@gmail.com

eBooks	Audiobooks	Fees/Services	Tours
Mobi, EPUB		No	No

Approximate turnaround time: ASAP
Where reviews are posted: Amazon, Goodreads, +Social
Languages: English

CATEGORIES

- **Fiction:** Cozy Mystery, Dystopian, Paranormal, Romance, YA
- **Nonfiction:** No
- **Excluded:** Christian, Comics, Erotica, Nonfiction

From the reviewer: I'm a SAHM with four children. Their ages are 13, 12, 10 and 9 months. I have 3 cats, 3 dogs and a pet rat. I enjoy reading when I have downtime.

BOOK BLOGGERS

Just Reviews (B9-111)

https://tillie49.wordpress.com
Fran Lewis | riffyone@optonlinel.net

eBooks	Audiobooks	Fees/Services	Tours
No		Yes	Yes

Approximate turnaround time: <3 wk
Where reviews are posted: Amazon, Goodreads, Scoop It, +Social
Languages: English

CATEGORIES

- **Fiction:** Fiction-General, Historical Fiction, Mystery, Paranormal, Science Fiction, Thriller, YA
- **Nonfiction:** Yes, Autobiography, Cookbooks, History, Memoirs, True Crime
- **Excluded:** Erotica, Self-Help

From the reviewer: Fran worked in the NYC Public Schools as the Reading and Writing Staff Developer for over 36 years. She has three masters Degrees and a PD in Supervision and Administration. Currently, she is a member of Who's Who of America's Teachers and Who's Who of America's Executives from Cambridge. In addition, she is the author of three children's books and a fourth that has just been published on Alzheimer's disease in order to honor her mom and help create more awareness for a cure. The title of my new Alzheimer's book is Memories are Precious: Alzheimer's Journey; Ruth's story and Sharp as a Tack and Scrambled Eggs Which Describes Your Brain? Fran is the author of 11 titles. She was the musical director for shows in her school and ran the school's newspaper. Fran writes reviews for authors upon request and for several other sites. You can read some of my reviews on Ezine.com and on ijustfinished.com under the name Gabina. Her radion show is www.blogtalkradio.com

Kissing Backwards, Lesbian Lit Reviews (B9-112)

https://kissingbackwards.wordpress.com
Vicky | KissingBackwards@gmail.com

eBooks	Audiobooks	Fees/Services	Tours
Mobi		Inquire	Yes

Approximate turnaround time: 1 mo
Where reviews are posted: Amazon, Goodreads
Languages: English

CATEGORIES

- **Fiction:** LGBTQ (Lesbian-centric)
- **Nonfiction:** Yes, LGBTQ (Lesbian-centric)
- **Excluded:** All except those noted

From the reviewer: I'm a library technician, who when not devouring books watches way too many horror films. I also love tea, cats, and Jeopardy.

Kitty's Book Spot! (B9-114)

http://2kasmom.booklikes.com
2kasmom | https://www.facebook.com/kittysbookspot

eBooks	Audiobooks	Fees/Services	Tours
Kindle, Mobi	Yes	No	Yes

Approximate turnaround time: 120 days
Where reviews are posted: Amazon, Goodreads, Books-a-Million, BN, Kobo, iBooks, +Social
Languages: English

CATEGORIES

- **Fiction:** Erotica, MM Romance, Romance, YA
- **Nonfiction:** Yes, Cookbooks, Gaming
- **Excluded:** Dystopian, Historical, Horror

From the reviewer: I am a mother of 3, who loves to read and blog. I also run an annual blog party—ask me how you can be a part!

Kristi's Book Nook (B9-116)

http://kristisbooknook.blogspot.com
Kristi Bernard | kbernard817@gmail.com

eBooks	Audiobooks	Fees/Services	Tours
No		Yes	Yes

Approximate turnaround time: 3-6 mo
Where reviews are posted: Amazon, Goodreads, The Reading Room, +Social
Languages: English

CATEGORIES

- **Fiction:** Children's, Middle Grade
- **Nonfiction:** Yes, Children's
- **Excluded:** Erotica

From the reviewer: I am a parent, reviewer and writer.

Lady Amber's Reviews and PR (B9-117)

http://www.ladyambersreviews.com
Amber Garcia | agarcia6510w@gmail.com

eBooks	Audiobooks	Fees/Services	Tours
Mobi		Yes	Yes

Approximate turnaround time: 2-3 mo
Where reviews are posted: Amazon, Goodreads, BN, +Social
Languages: English

CATEGORIES

- **Fiction:** Most fiction considered
- **Nonfiction:** No
- **Excluded:** Children's, Christian, Comics, Historical Fiction, Horror, MG, Thriller, Westerns, Zombies

From the reviewer: I've been running Lady Amber's Reviews & PR for six years now. I love reading, writing and meeting new authors and readers.

Laurie Here-Contemporary Fiction & More (B9-118)

http://www.lauriehere.com

Laurie Carlson | laurieisreading@gmail.com

eBooks	Audiobooks	Fees/Services	Tours
Kindle, PDF		No	Yes

Approximate turnaround time: 1-2 mo

Where reviews are posted: Amazon, Goodreads, +Social

Languages: English

CATEGORIES

- **Fiction:** Amish, Chick Lit, Children's, Contemporary, Historical Fiction, Mystery, NA, Suspense, Thriller, Women's Fiction
- **Nonfiction:** Yes, Memoirs-Author, NASCAR
- **Excluded:** Autobiography, Biography, Erotica, Graphic novels, Horror, Memoirs, Middle Grade, Science Fiction, Urban Fantasy, Vampires, Werewolf, YA, Zombies

From the reviewer: I read and blog about books. That's what I do besides throwing junk away (I'm shredding tons of old paperwork so we can move out of this house!). I have a very rare neurological muscle disease that makes it so I cannot work anymore, so doing this blog about books helps to keep my mind alert and happy. I don't know what I'd do without it!

Library of Clean Reads (B9-121)

http://www.libraryofcleanreads.com
Laura Fabiani | breezagirl@gmail.com

eBooks	Audiobooks	Fees/Services	Tours
Yes		Yes	Yes

Approximate turnaround time: 2 mo
Where reviews are posted: Amazon, Goodreads, BN
Languages: English

CATEGORIES

- **Fiction:** Most fiction considered
- **Nonfiction:** Yes
- **Excluded:** Erotica, Horror, LGBTQ, Paranormal, Religion, Vampires

From the reviewer: I've been book blogging for eight years and I'm an eclectic reader with a background in social services, child psychology, and book marketing.

Literary Meanderings (B9-122)

http://www.literaryme.net
Sarah | sarahbookish@gmail.com

eBooks	Audiobooks	Fees/Services	Tours
Kindle, PDF		No	Yes

Approximate turnaround time: 1 mo
Where reviews are posted: Amazon, Goodreads, +Social
Languages: English

CATEGORIES

- **Fiction:** Contemporary, Contemporary Romance, Dystopian, Historical Fiction, Historical Romance, NA, Paranormal, Science Fiction, Urban Fantasy, YA
- **Nonfiction:** No
- **Excluded:** Children's, Comics, Erotica, Nonfiction, Picture Books

From the reviewer: I am a college student and work a full-time job. I am also gay, so if you have any lesbian romance to throw my way, I would love to review for you! In addition to reviews, I also run interviews, guest posts, book highlights, giveaways, etc. I can set up anything you want if your book is something I would like to promote, at no cost, of course!

Little Miss Bookmark (B9-123)

http://www.LittleMissBookmark.blogspot.com
Julie | Use website contact form

eBooks	**Audiobooks**	**Fees/Services**	**Tours**
Mobi, PDF		No	Yes

Approximate turnaround time: 1-2 mo
Where reviews are posted: Amazon, Goodreads, BN, +Social
Languages: English

CATEGORIES

- **Fiction:** Erotica, Mystery, NA, Paranormal, Romance, Thriller, YA
- **Nonfiction:** No
- **Excluded:** Children's, Horror, Science Fiction

From the reviewer: I'm a stay at home mom of two school aged boys... so really, I'm just a lazy lady without a job that likes to live vicariously through these fictional characters while my boys are at school and there is actually peace and quiet around here.

BOOK BLOGGERS

Livres et Biscuits (B9-124)

http://livresetbiscuits.blogspot.com/
Malak Ismail | livresetbiscuits@gmail.com

eBooks	Audiobooks	Fees/Services	Tours
EPUB, PDF		No	No

Approximate turnaround time: 2 mo
Where reviews are posted: Goodreads, +Social
Languages: English, French

CATEGORIES

- **Fiction:** Classics, Crime, Fairy Tales, Fantasy, Historical Fiction, Horror, Science Fiction
- **Nonfiction:** Yes, Medicine, Philosophy, Politics, Science
- **Excluded:** Erotica, Religion

From the reviewer: My name is Malak Ismail. I am the administrator of Livres et Biscuits, living in Montreal, Quebec, Canada. Despite my scientific backgroun, I am very interested in literature and plays. Livres et Biscuits was created to share my passion for books with people. The blog is bilingual and reviews are written in the original language of the books as much as possible. I started this blog in December 2010 in order to share my opinions and the joys of reading. I do not consider myself an expert in all types of books that I read; I just give my opinion.

Lola's Reviews (B9-125)

http://lolasreviews.com/
Lola | lolabookreviews@gmail.com

eBooks	**Audiobooks**	**Fees/Services**	**Tours**
Mobi, EPUB		No	Yes

Approximate turnaround time: 1 wk-2 mo
Where reviews are posted: Amazon, Goodreads, BN, Kobo, +Social
Languages: English

CATEGORIES

- **Fiction:** Contemporary Romance, Cozy Mystery, Dystopian, Erotica, Fantasy, Fiction-General, Historical Fiction, Middle Grade, NA, Paranormal Romance, Romance, Science Fiction, Steampunk, Urban Fantasy
- **Nonfiction:** Yes, Book Marketing, Coloring Books, Publishing
- **Excluded:** Horror, Thriller

From the reviewer: I love to read a variety of genres and am often willing to branch out into new to me genres if a book sounds good. I also have an interest in book marketing. I love cooking and baking and will occasionally blog about that too.

BOOK BLOGGERS

Long and Short Reviews (B9-238)

http://www.longandshortreviews.com
Marianne Arkins (primary contact) | http://tinyurl.com/ybuz6sf3

eBooks	Audiobooks	Fees/Services	Tours
PDF		No	Yes

Approximate turnaround time: Inquire
Where reviews are posted: Amazon, Goodreads
Languages: English

CATEGORIES

- **Fiction:** Most fiction considered
- **Nonfiction:** No
- **Excluded:** Non-Fiction, Poetry

From the reviewer: About Us

* Long and Short Reviews opened its doors August 27, 2007

* As of 12/31/12 we've reviewed more than 8900 books and short stories

* As of 12/31/12 we receive over 600 visitors / 1500 page views daily*

* We may be contacted at lasreviews@gmail.com

* We are a "snark free" reviews site.

Love between the Sheets (B9-128)

http://readlovelust.com
Natalie, Mary, Meagan, Christina, Cindy and Julie
booklovebetweenthesheets@gmail.com

eBooks	Audiobooks	Fees/Services	Tours
Kindle	Yes	No	Yes

Approximate turnaround time: 1-2 mo
Where reviews are posted: Amazon, Goodreads, +Social
Languages: English

CATEGORIES

- **Fiction:** Contemporary Romance, Erotica, NA, Paranormal Romance, Romance, Urban Fantasy, YA
- **Nonfiction:** No
- **Excluded:** Christian Romance, Historical Romance

From the reviewer: We are six friends who share a love of reading. We each come from different backgrounds and have varied interests.

Making it Happen (B9-129)

http://moonangel23.blogspot.com

Carra Saigh | makingithappenblog@gmail.com

eBooks	Audiobooks	Fees/Services	Tours
Mobi, EPUB, PDF		Yes	Yes

Approximate turnaround time: 6-8 wk

Where reviews are posted: Amazon, Goodreads, BN, iBooks

Languages: English

CATEGORIES

- **Fiction:** Contemporary Romance, Crime, Erotica, Fantasy, Historical Romance, Horror, NA, Paranormal, Romance, Science Fiction, Thriller, YA
- **Nonfiction:** No
- **Excluded:** Children's, Comics, Nonfiction, Religious

From the reviewer: I've been a voracious reader since I was about 6 years old, and when not working or sleeping, I can usually be found with a book in my hand. On average, I read 5-7 books a week. I originally started my blog in 2009 as a way to chronicle my weight loss and foray into the world of running and half-marathons, but then transitioned over to book reviews and promotion in early 2014. My favorite genres are paranormal and contemporary romance, and I enjoy discovering new authors, especially all the amazing indie authors out there! I'm known for my honest feedback and reviews, sometimes blatantly honest, and I'm a stickler for basic grammar and spelling in finished books (ARCs I review strictly on content).

BOOK BLOGGERS

Mallory Reads (B9-130)

http://www.malloryreadsblog.wordpress.com
Mallory de Man | http://www.malloryreadsblog.wordpress.com

eBooks	Audiobooks	Fees/Services	Tours
Kindle, PDF	No	No	Yes

Approximate turnaround time: 1 mo
Where reviews are posted: Amazon, Goodreads
Languages: English, Dutch

CATEGORIES

- **Fiction:** Drama, Erotica, Fantasy, Mystery, Romance, Thriller, YA
- **Nonfiction:** No
- **Excluded:** Autobiography, Biography, Historical Fiction, Poetry, Religious

From the reviewer: I am a 20-year-old Dutchie, I love reading any most books as long as the story line is good. I will always give an honest review and post your book on my blog. I can do some promotional material as well.

MaryD Reviews (B9-131)

http://marydreviews.ausxip.com
MaryD | http://marydreviews.ausxip.com/contact

eBooks	Audiobooks	Fees/Services	Tours
Kindle, EPUB		No	No

Approximate turnaround time: 1-2 mo
Where reviews are posted: Amazon, Goodreads, +Social
Languages: English

CATEGORIES

- **Fiction:** Clean Romance, LGBTQ (Lesbian-centric), Mystery, Suspense, YA
- **Nonfiction:** Yes
- **Excluded:** BDSM, Comics, Dystopian, Erotica, Horror, Incest, Paranormal, Rape

From the reviewer: I'm an author of six novels, a webmaster, and graphic designer for twenty years. I love great stories and promoting authors. Gladly promote authors whose work I love.

Matthew R. Bell's BookBlogBonanza (B9-132)

http://www.matthewrbel.blogspot.co.uk/
Matthew R. Bell | Use website contact form

eBooks	Audiobooks	Fees/Services	Tours
Kindle		No	Inquire

Approximate turnaround time: 3-5 days
Where reviews are posted: Amazon, Goodreads, +Social
Languages: English

CATEGORIES

- **Fiction:** Most fiction considered
- **Nonfiction:** No
- **Excluded:** Erotica, Nonfiction, Religious

From the reviewer: I am a writer-in-training with an insatiable love for works of fiction.

Metaphors and Moonlight (B9-133)

http://blog.kristenburns.com/
Kristen | http://blog.kristenburns.com/review-policy

eBooks	Audiobooks	Fees/Services	Tours
Mobi, EPUB		No	No

Approximate turnaround time: 3 mo
Where reviews are posted: Amazon, Goodreads, +Social
Languages: English

CATEGORIES

- **Fiction:** Fantasy, Graphic novels, NA, Paranormal, Romance, Science Fiction, YA
- **Nonfiction:** No
- **Excluded:** Anything outside of the fantasy and science fiction genres.

From the reviewer: I love reading both fantasy and science fiction in a variety of age ranges, and I'm always looking for the next great book to share with everyone! I'm also open to hosting giveaways and having guest posts if any authors are interested.

MichaelSciFan (B9-134)

http://www.michaelscifan.us
Michael | http://tinyurl.com/ya8zmyc8

eBooks	Audiobooks	Fees/Services	Tours
Kindle	Yes	No	Yes

Approximate turnaround time: 3 mo
Where reviews are posted: Amazon, Goodreads, Audible, +Social
Languages: English

CATEGORIES

- **Fiction:** Dystopian, Fantasy, Romance, Science Fiction, YA
- **Nonfiction:** No
- **Excluded:** Erotica, Horror, Mystery, Nonfiction, Thriller

From the reviewer: I am an avid reader of science fiction and fantasy. I put together this blog to provide information on books and authors that interest me in the hope that it will help others with similar interests. I tend to seek out new and upcoming authors, but I also enjoy mainstream series as well.

Midwest Book Review (B9-135)

http://www.midwestbookreview.com
James A. Cox | mbr@execpc.com

eBooks	Audiobooks	Fees/Services	Tours
(For a fee)		Yes	No

Approximate turnaround time: 8-10 wk
Where reviews are posted: Book Review Index (Gale Cengage Learning)
Languages: English

CATEGORIES

- **Fiction:** Most fiction considered
- **Nonfiction:** Yes, Architecture, Art, Arts & Crafts, Biography, Cookbooks, History, Military, Needlecraft, Science, Sports
- **Excluded:** Erotica

From the reviewer: I've been the editor-in-chief of the Midwest Book Review for the last 40 years. [Editor's note: If your book passes initial screening, but cannot be read due to their schedule, you may submit a review from another source (with permission) and they will run it in their monthly book review publication Reviewer's Bookwatch, under that reviewer's byline. Finally, MBR charges a reader fee for reviewing ebooks, pre-publication manuscripts, galleys, uncorrected proofs, ARCs, and pdf files.]

Misty103@HubPages (B9-136)

http://hubpages.com/@misty103

Sefina Hawke | http://hubpages.com/@misty103

eBooks	Audiobooks	Fees/Services	Tours
Kindle	Yes	Inquire	Yes

Approximate turnaround time: 1-2 mo

Where reviews are posted: Amazon, Goodreads, +Social

Languages: English, French, some Spanish

CATEGORIES

- **Fiction:** Most fiction considered
- **Nonfiction:** Yes, Cookbooks, Psychology, Self-Help
- **Excluded:** Inquire

From the reviewer: I am a psychology major and child's counselor; I love getting children's books and I am always open to a new psychology book.

Molly Lolly-Reader, Reviewer, Lover of Words (B9-137)

https://mollylollyauthor.wordpress.com

Molly Lolly | https://mollylollyauthor.wordpress.com/contact-molly

eBooks	Audiobooks	Fees/Services	Tours
Mobi, PDF		No	Yes

Approximate turnaround time: 1 mo

Where reviews are posted: Goodreads

Languages: English

CATEGORIES

- **Fiction:** Erotica, LGBTQ, Romance
- **Nonfiction:** No
- **Excluded:** Nonfiction

From the reviewer: I'm a wife and a mom living overseas on a military base out in the wilds. I love romance as my escape for when they times get tough as my spouse deploys or has a crazy schedule when not. I love promoting books so even if I wind up passing on a review I usually offer promotional space for books that align with the blog. I love hosting guest posts and other exclusive content as well so those spots are always open as well.

BOOK BLOGGERS

MoonShine Art Spot (B9-139)

http://moonshineartspot.blogspot.com
Lisa | MoonShineArtSpot@gmail.com

eBooks	Audiobooks	Fees/Services	Tours
Kindle, EPUB		Yes	Yes

Approximate turnaround time: few wk to mo
Where reviews are posted: Amazon, Goodreads, +Social
Languages: English

CATEGORIES

- **Fiction:** Dystopian, Science Fiction, Supernatural, YA
- **Nonfiction:** Yes, Children's
- **Excluded:** Comics, Erotica, Graphic Novels

From the reviewer: We participate in Rafflecopter giveaways if the author plans to provide a copy of the book to the winner. This service includes a spotlight, an interview, or whatever the author wants highlighted about them and their book on the page.

More Than a Review (B9-140)

http://www.morethanareview.com/
Carol, Bethany, Sonie and Pat | http://tinyurl.com/ybo27ozp

eBooks	Audiobooks	Fees/Services	Tours
Kindle, EPUB, PDF		Yes	No

Approximate turnaround time: 1-2 mo
Where reviews are posted: Amazon, Goodreads, BN
Languages: English

CATEGORIES

- **Fiction:** Christian Fiction, Mystery, Romance, Suspense, Thriller, YA
- **Nonfiction:** Yes, Biography, True Crime
- **Excluded:** Erotica, Horror, LGBTQ

From the reviewer: My name is Donna, and I am an avid reader who felt the need for a book review site that provided more than an overall rating. At More Than a Review, we allow reviewers to share the content levels for sex, violence, language, and drugs or alcohol. The content ratings help readers find books that are best suited to their interests. Be surprised by plot twists, not objectionable content.

Mrs. Mommy Booknerd's
Book Reviews (B9-141)

http://mrsmommybooknerd.blogspot.com

Emily Lewis | mrsmommybooknerdsbookreviews@gmail.com

eBooks	Audiobooks	Fees/Services	Tours
Kindle		Yes	Yes

Approximate turnaround time: 1-3 mo

Where reviews are posted: Amazon, Goodreads, +Social

Languages: English

CATEGORIES

- **Fiction:** Children's, Fantasy, Fiction-General, Mystery, Romance, Science Fiction, Thriller, YA
- **Nonfiction:** Yes, Arts, Biography, Cookbooks, Crafting, Entertainment, Fitness, Food, Health, History, Memoirs, Photography, Self-Help, Wine
- **Excluded:** Erotica

From the reviewer: MEET Emily (Founder of MMBBR, site manager and lead blogger) AKA MRS. MOMMY BOOKNERD Blog Founded in 2011 Email: mrsmommybooknerdsbookreviews@gmail.com I like to share the gift of a good read with others, so I started this blog. I marvel at writers and the journey they can take you on through the pages of a book. I am a mother of 2 fantastic young boys, a book nerd, a wife, a growth and development teacher for children ages 2-5 and fitness instructor. I am passionate about being a mother and about books. I feel instilling the love of reading in my children is giving them a lifelong gift. Stats: I am part of the SheReads Blog Network. I am in the top 1% of reviewers on Goodreads. I am a top reviewer on Amazon. I am part of Influenster. NOTE: I have developed a class entitled Art Through Stories.

Musings From An Addicted Reader (B9-142)

https://musingsfromanaddictedreader.wordpress.com/
Emily | https://musingsfromanaddictedreader.wordpress.com/

eBooks	Audiobooks	Fees/Services	Tours
Kindle, Mobi, PDF	Yes	No	Yes

Approximate turnaround time: 1 mo
Where reviews are posted: Amazon, Goodreads, +Social
Languages: English

CATEGORIES

- **Fiction:** Contemporary, Erotica, Fantasy, Historical Fiction, Paranormal, Romance, Suspense, Thriller, YA
- **Nonfiction:** Yes
- **Excluded:** Horror

From the reviewer: I work from home and spend a huge part of my time reading. Always looking for new authors to discover and new books from favorite authors.

Musings of a Snickerdoodle (B9-239)

http://snickerdoodlesmusings.blogspot.com/
Sarah Lambert | snickerdoodlesbookreviews@gmail.com

eBooks	Audiobooks	Fees/Services	Tours
Kindle, Mobi	Yes	No	No

Approximate turnaround time: Inquire
Where reviews are posted: Amazon, Goodreads, LibraryThing, https://bookelucidator.blogspot.com/
Languages: English

CATEGORIES

- **Fiction:** Christian Historical Fiction
- **Nonfiction:** Yes, Autobiography, Bible Study, Biography, Christian, History
- **Excluded:** Erotica

From the reviewer: I am a Christian blogger who reads and critiques many Christian books. My dad is a pastor and I often have discussions with him on what I love about a book or what I am critical of while reading these books. I am also quite interested in biographies and other history books as well (Christian and non-Christian). I do not guarantee that I will like any given book. If I agree to review a book you can be sure that I will give an honest opinion as to why I like or dislike the book.

My Guilty Obsession Book Blog (B9-144)

http://www.myguiltyobsession.com
Christina | mygltyobsession@outlook.com

eBooks	Audiobooks	Fees/Services	Tours
Kindle, Mobi, iBooks		No	Yes

Approximate turnaround time: 1-2 wk
Where reviews are posted: Amazon, Goodreads, +Social
Languages: English

CATEGORIES

- **Fiction:** Contemporary Romance, Crime, Erotica, Horror, NA, Sports
- **Nonfiction:** No
- **Excluded:** Nonfiction, Paranormal, Science Fiction

From the reviewer: I am a mom of two children, working part time in the medical field and started my blog a year after I discovered my passion for reading romance novels and the Indie world.

My Life. One Story at a Time. (B9-145)

https://www.mylifeonestoryatatime.com
Donna McBroom-Theriot | mylife.onestoryatatime@gmail.com

eBooks	Audiobooks	Fees/Services	Tours
Kindle, Mobi		No	No

Approximate turnaround time: 1-2 mo
Where reviews are posted: Amazon, Goodreads, +Social
Languages: English

CATEGORIES
- **Fiction:** Chick Lit, Contemporary Romance, Historical Romance, Romance
- **Nonfiction:** Yes, Cookbooks, Devotionals, Memoirs
- **Excluded:** Elementary, Erotica, Graphic, Horror, Middle Grade, Paranormal, Poetry, Science Fiction, Verse, YA

From the reviewer: I love reading and have been reviewing books for a number of years. I also enjoy running giveaways via the Rafflecopter on my site. Have a book promotion? I'll be glad to help you promote (please check accepted genres.)

My Tangled Skeins Book Reviews (B9-146)

http://mytangledskeinsbookreviews.blogspot.com
Amanda Price | mytangledskeinsbookreview@gmail.com

eBooks	Audiobooks	Fees/Services	Tours
Kindle, EPUB, PDF		Yes	Yes

Approximate turnaround time: Inquire
Where reviews are posted: Amazon, Goodreads, LibraryThing, +Social
Languages: English

CATEGORIES
- **Fiction:** Most fiction considered
- **Nonfiction:** Yes
- **Excluded:** None

From the reviewer: I am a mom, a crafter, a gamer, and an avid book reader.

Nicely Phrased (B9-147)

http://nicelyphrasedbookblog.com/
Adrienne and Emma | nicelyphrasedbookblog@gmail.com

eBooks	Audiobooks	Fees/Services	Tours
Kindle		No	Yes

Approximate turnaround time: 1-2 mo
Where reviews are posted: Amazon, Goodreads, +Social
Languages: English

CATEGORIES

- **Fiction:** Contemporary Romance, Erotica, Fantasy, NA, Paranormal, YA
- **Nonfiction:** No
- **Excluded:** Biography, Christian, Science Fiction

From the reviewer: We're a mother-daughter blogging team. Emma loves young adult books that aren't romance-driven. Adrienne loves all different types of romance. We also love to host giveaways! We're both always excited to meet readers and authors!

Nighttime Reading Center (B9-148)

http://www.Nrcbooks.blogspot.com
Lindsay Hickey | Ben200608@gmail.com

eBooks	Audiobooks	Fees/Services	Tours
Kindle, Nook	Yes	Yes	Yes

Approximate turnaround time: 1-2 mo
Where reviews are posted: Amazon, Goodreads, +Social
Languages: English

CATEGORIES

- **Fiction:** Amish, Children's, Christian Fiction, Classics, Fiction-General, Historical Fiction, Military, Mystery, Romance, Women's Fiction, YA
- **Nonfiction:** Yes, Biography, Memoirs
- **Excluded:** Erotica, How-To, Self-Help, Travel

From the reviewer: I love animals and own 3 cats. I will start putting my reviews on this blog as of this week and weekend. I now have three step brothers. I met two of them. I call them brothers. I met two of them. I call them brothers. Their names are Montana and Sean. I now have a step mother as well. I do talk to her as well. Her name is Jenise. I will be traveling between Pa and FL through the years. You can contact me.

BOOK BLOGGERS

Oh My Bookness (B9-150)

https://plus.google.com/+OhMyBookness
Brittany Perez | Bperezbookreviews@gmail.com

eBooks	Audiobooks	Fees/Services	Tours
EPUB, PDF		No	No

Approximate turnaround time: 2-3 mo
Where reviews are posted: Amazon, Goodreads, Blogger, +Social
Languages: English, Spanish

CATEGORIES

- **Fiction:** Most fiction considered
- **Nonfiction:** Yes, Biography, Children's, Cookbooks, Graphic Design, History, How-To, LGBTQ, Memoirs, Music, Painting, Political, Sports, True Crime
- **Excluded:** Erotica

From the reviewer: I'm an avid book reader and love the feel of having an actual book in my hand. An e-book cannot replace having the actual physical book copy fitting in your hand or flipping through the pages, piece of memory always being left behind always left behind on the cover, page no matter how well you take care. If it's a crease, small tear, place holder, small note, underline, or crease in the spine or coloring from age, the memories a physical copy leaves us will never be in the same category as e-book, though they do have a place and time and convenience, but will never completely replace. I have a large selection of books ranging from hard copies and paper backs, to e-books. The number of physical books is overwhelming to the room but that's what makes it so great cause you can always go back say "I remember when I first read this, it was in 5th grade", "10th" in my 20's and so, to age some of my books. I like to keep expanding on my own library, in both physical and digital. I like to share what I read with others cause of my large collection, I would like to write a review about all my books but sadly I can't, so I will try to share with you as many as I can and discoveries of books that I find to be fascinating or oddly fun, and hope you may find to some helpful or insightful into your next literary journey. You will find here books ranging from mystery, sci-fi, fiction, non-fiction, teen-fiction, children books, biography, history, fantasy, to name a few.

Old Fox Reviews (B9-151)

https://oldfoxblog.wordpress.com
Jessica | https://oldfoxblog.wordpress.com/contact

eBooks	Audiobooks	Fees/Services	Tours
Kindle		No	No

Approximate turnaround time: 1-2 mo
Where reviews are posted: Goodreads
Languages: English

CATEGORIES

- **Fiction:** Fantasy, Fiction-General, Thriller, YA
- **Nonfiction:** No
- **Excluded:** Erotica, Nonfiction

From the reviewer: I don't quite know what I want to be when I grow up (ahem-I'm only 30). Some days I'm a writer, editor, reader; other days, I'm a graphic designer, computer programmer, animal lover. Actually, I'm always an animal lover. I might not know my dream occupation, but I know my favorite place is on the front porch on a warm day, cup of coffee, cat in my lap, reading a good book.

Olivia's Catastrophe (B9-152)

http://olivia-savannah.blogspot.nl/
Olivia | lonelysearchforever@gmail.com

eBooks	Audiobooks	Fees/Services	Tours
Kindle		No	Yes

Approximate turnaround time: 2 mo
Where reviews are posted: Amazon, Goodreads, +Social
Languages: English

CATEGORIES

- **Fiction:** Action, Contemporary, Fantasy, NA, Paranormal, Romance, Science Fiction, YA
- **Nonfiction:** Yes, Autobiography, Biography
- **Excluded:** Comics

From the reviewer: I am a student who loves to read, write, and play basketball. If you send a print copy, I am more likely to get to your review faster. I also love hosting giveaways!

BOOK BLOGGERS

On Writing (B9-153)

http://www.onwriting.in/
Saurabh Garg | http://www.onwriting.in/contact/

eBooks	Audiobooks	Fees/Services	Tours
Kindle		No	No

Approximate turnaround time: 1-2 wk
Where reviews are posted: Social
Languages: English

CATEGORIES

- **Fiction:** Romance, Thriller, Travel
- **Nonfiction:** Yes, Biography, Business
- **Excluded:** Comics, Religion, YA

From the reviewer: I am a published writer working on my next book. I am happy to swap reviews!

Once Upon An Alpha (B9-154)

http://onceuponanalpha.com
Shannon Hunt and Michelle Dare | onceuponanalpha@gmail.com

eBooks	Audiobooks	Fees/Services	Tours
Kindle, iBooks		Yes	Yes

Approximate turnaround time: 1-2 mo
Where reviews are posted: Amazon, Goodreads
Languages: English

CATEGORIES

- **Fiction:** Erotica, Romance
- **Nonfiction:** Yes, Cookbooks, Crafting
- **Excluded:** Biography, Religion

From the reviewer: We are a book blog that likes to talk about all things bookish and romance.

OnDBookshelf (B9-155)

http://www.ondbookshelf.com
Donna | OnDBookshelf@gmail.com

eBooks	Audiobooks	Fees/Services	Tours
Kindle	Yes	No	Yes

Approximate turnaround time: 1-2 mo
Where reviews are posted: Amazon, Goodreads, +Social
Languages: English

CATEGORIES

- **Fiction:** Contemporary, Historical Fiction, Literary Fiction, Women's Fiction, YA
- **Nonfiction:** Yes, Memoirs
- **Excluded:** Erotica, Horror, Paranormal

From the reviewer: Stay at home mom to two teenage girls. Read 2-3 books per week on average.

PC Book Reviews (B9-156)

http://www.pcbookreviews.com/
Iris Hunter | http://www.pcbookreviews.com/contact/

eBooks	Audiobooks	Fees/Services	Tours
EPUB, PDF		Yes	Yes

Approximate turnaround time: 1 mo
Where reviews are posted: Amazon, Goodreads, +Social
Languages: English

CATEGORIES

- **Fiction:** Erotica, Fantasy, Paranormal, Paranormal Romance, Urban Fantasy
- **Nonfiction:** No
- **Excluded:** Horror

From the reviewer: I am a mom and art director and I love to read books with a happy ending. Some of my favorite authors include Ann Aguirre, J.R. Ward, Nalini Singh, Erin McCarthy, Christine Feehan, Kresely Cole, Jeaniene Frost, Darynda Jones, Dianne Duvall, and Jenn Bennett. I launched this site in 2010, but I first began reviewing books years ago. I offer book-related features, reviews, giveaways, interviews, guest posts, and so much more. I have also launched book tours to help authors promote their books on blogs.

Perusing Princesses (B9-157)

http://www.perusingprincesses.net
Elizabeth, Kelly and Emma | http://tinyurl.com/y7yrs5wb

eBooks	Audiobooks	Fees/Services	Tours
Kindle		Yes	Yes

Approximate turnaround time: 2 wk
Where reviews are posted: Amazon, Goodreads, Blogger, WordPress, Rebel-Mouse, Tint, NetGalley, +Social
Languages: English

CATEGORIES

- **Fiction:** Romance
- **Nonfiction:** No
- **Excluded:** Biography, Christian, Comics, Dystopian, Fantasy, Historical, Nonfiction, Paranormal, Steampunk, YA

From the reviewer: We are three self-proclaimed Princesses who love to read, review, and share! We still love fairy tales; they are just a little bit dirtier now…

Pirate Lady Pages (B9-158)

https://pirateladypages.wordpress.com
Keira | keira.signingon@gmail.com

eBooks	Audiobooks	Fees/Services	Tours
Kindle, Mobi		No	Yes

Approximate turnaround time: 1-2 mo
Where reviews are posted: Amazon, Goodreads, +Social
Languages: English, German

CATEGORIES

- **Fiction:** Contemporary, Fantasy, Graphic novels, Historical Fiction, Middle Grade, Science Fiction, Short Stories, YA
- **Nonfiction:** Yes, Psychology, Sociology
- **Excluded:** Christian, Comics, Erotica, Horror, Manga

From the reviewer: I love blogging, writing and reading all sorts. Fantasy, however, is my favorite thing to read!

POTL Blog (B9-159)

https://princessofthelight.wordpress.com/
Mr. N and Mrs. N. | nnlight@outlook.com

eBooks	Audiobooks	Fees/Services	Tours
Kindle, PDF		Yes	Yes

Approximate turnaround time: ~12 wk
Where reviews are posted: Amazon, Goodreads, BN, Kobo, +Social
Languages: English

CATEGORIES

- **Fiction:** Children's, Contemporary, Fantasy, Historical Fiction, Horror, Mystery, Paranormal, Romance, Suspense, Women's Fiction, YA
- **Nonfiction:** Yes, Biography, Business, Cookbooks, History, Inspirational, Memoirs, Photography, Spirituality, Sports
- **Excluded:** Abuse, Assault, Drug Use, Violence

From the reviewer: Greetings, book lovers! I love books and am pleased to offer Author Promotion Services. I'm a professional social media marketer by trade and I have the potential reach of over forty-million followers (yes, many of those are readers). My followers trust my opinion and if I tell them a book/blog is great, they will often check it out. Many readers discover new authors via word of mouth, especially quality honest book reviews and author interviews. I love promoting authors and this is a great way to get exposure for you and your book. Together, we can increase your sales and gain new readers.

Rainbow Gold Reviews (B9-163)

http://www.rainbowgoldreviews.wordpress.com
Marc and Bethany | http://tinyurl.com/y9mo8wsk

eBooks	Audiobooks	Fees/Services	Tours
Kindle, PDF	Yes	No	Yes

Approximate turnaround time: Inquire
Where reviews are posted: Amazon, Goodreads, +Social
Languages: English

CATEGORIES

- **Fiction:** LGBTQ
- **Nonfiction:** No
- **Excluded:** Heterosexual Fiction

From the reviewer: Our reviewers are from Europe and North America. We love LGBT fiction and support and celebrate equality. We are happy to promote stories, authors, and publishers we love and aim to always give our honest opinions in a respectful way.

Read Between the Lines (B9-164)

http://www.rbtlreviews.com
Anna | sadase98@gmail.com

eBooks	Audiobooks	Fees/Services	Tours
Mobi		Yes	Yes

Approximate turnaround time: 1-2 mo
Where reviews are posted: Amazon
Languages: English

CATEGORIES

- **Fiction:** Dystopian, Erotica, Fiction-General, NA, Paranormal, Steampunk, YA
- **Nonfiction:** Yes
- **Excluded:** Children's, Christian, Horror, Science Fiction

From the reviewer: I am an avid reader from Pennsylvania. My name is Anna and I am a book reading, book buying, book-loving person! My belief in people who do not read are truly missing out on something wonderful. Reading broadens your mind! My goal is to share my love of reading with the world one book at a time. If there is a good book out there, I will find it and share it with you. I have had a love of reading since I was a little girl and my love of books has not changed. I am often told by friends and loved ones (especially my husband) that I live in a library (but it is also said friends and loved ones that help me feed my addiction for they continue to buy me books) which is fine by me. I started this blog to share my love of reading with everyone. So, I hope you will grab a drink, sit back and join me on this journey of discovering new and amazing books. There is nothing like sitting down with a hot cup of tea (which is my choice of beverage) and a book to read.

Reading After Dark (B9-166)

http://www.ReadingAfterDark.com
April | http://www.readingafterdark.com/review-request/

eBooks	Audiobooks	Fees/Services	Tours
Kindle, iBooks		Inquire	Yes

Approximate turnaround time: 1-2 mo
Where reviews are posted: Amazon, Goodreads, +Social
Languages: English

CATEGORIES

- **Fiction:** Chick Lit, Contemporary, Erotica, NA, Romance
- **Nonfiction:** Yes
- **Excluded:** Philosophical, Political, Religious, Self-Help

From the reviewer: I've always been an avid reader. Blogging seems like a great way to connect with the book community. If you have an idea on how we can work together (like I said before) contact me and let's chat.

Reading for the Stars and Moon (B9-167)

http://adultreadingforthestarsmoon.blogspot.com
Chelsea Hunter | Use website contact form

eBooks	Audiobooks	Fees/Services	Tours
Mobi		No	Yes

Approximate turnaround time: 1-2 mo
Where reviews are posted: Amazon, Goodreads
Languages: English

CATEGORIES

- **Fiction:** Fiction-General, NA
- **Nonfiction:** No
- **Excluded:** Erotica, Middle Grade, YA

From the reviewer: I am a college student who loves to read books in my free time. I am more than willing to promote your book however I can: guest post, interview, review, giveaway, etc.

Readper (B9-169)

http://readper.com
Jaxon Reed | http://readper.com/authors

eBooks	Audiobooks	Fees/Services	Tours
Kindle		Yes	No

Approximate turnaround time: 1-3 mo
Where reviews are posted: Amazon
Languages: English

CATEGORIES

- **Fiction:** Fantasy, Science Fiction, Thriller
- **Nonfiction:** No
- **Excluded:** Erotica

From the reviewer: Readper is a book promotion blog run by author Jaxon Reed featuring romance, science fiction, thrillers, and more. The Readper weekly newsletter goes out to email subscribers every Saturday and promotes books featured on the blog and selected Amazon titles.

Red Cheeks Reads (B9-170)

http://www.redcheeksreads.com
Amie and Miranda | redcheeksreads@gmail.com

eBooks	Audiobooks	Fees/Services	Tours
Kindle		No	Yes

Approximate turnaround time: 1-2 mo
Where reviews are posted: Amazon, Goodreads, BN, +Social
Languages: English

CATEGORIES

- **Fiction:** Contemporary Romance, Erotica, NA, Paranormal, Romance
- **Nonfiction:** No
- **Excluded:** Christian Fiction, Comics, Nonfiction

From the reviewer: We are two moms who love romance. We read, review, and promote. We are happy to run giveaways and love to help authors promote their work.

Redpillows (B9-171)

https://redpillows.wordpress.com/
Namrata Ganti | reviews.redpillows@gmail.com

eBooks	Audiobooks	Fees/Services	Tours
Kindle		No	No

Approximate turnaround time: 1-2 mo
Where reviews are posted: Amazon, Goodreads, +Social
Languages: English

CATEGORIES

- **Fiction:** Action, Clean Romance, Contemporary Romance, Drama, Fantasy, Historical Fiction, Humor, Middle Grade, Mystery, Thriller, YA
- **Nonfiction:** Yes, Autobiography, Biography, Memoirs
- **Excluded:** Christian Fiction, Erotica

From the reviewer: I am an engineer working for Bosch, in the automotive domain. Reading is my hobby and passion. As a result, I spend my free time reading books and sharing my opinion about them. This ensures that the author and book gain publicity and is a way for people to judge whether they want to read the book. I also took up promotions and interviews with authors! My blog is all about books!

Reviews by Cat Ellington (B9-172)

https://catellingtonblog.wordpress.com/
Cat Ellington | https://catellingtonblog.wordpress.com

eBooks	Audiobooks	Fees/Services	Tours
EPUB		No	No

Approximate turnaround time: Inquire
Where reviews are posted: Amazon, Goodreads, BN, NetGalley, +Social
Languages: English

CATEGORIES

- **Fiction:** Apocalyptic, Chick Lit, Comics, Crime, Erotica, Graphic novels, Horror, Paranormal, Romance, Suspense, Thriller, Urban Fantasy
- **Nonfiction:** Yes, Autobiography, Memoirs
- **Excluded:** Western, YA

From the reviewer: Aside from my life as a public figure with dual careers in entertainment as a multi-genre songwriter/composer in the music industry, and as a casting director of feature films in the motion picture industry, I also moonlight in the art world as a professional art model, and in the field of literature as an author of expressive poetry. In my private life, however, I am an impassioned bookworm who loves to both read and review novels of literary fiction and nonfiction-hence my adored leisure as an artistic member of the two social cataloging sites, Goodreads and Netgalley.

BOOK BLOGGERS

Reviews In A Pinch (B9-174)

http://reviewsinapinch.com
Mel | reviewsinapinch@gmail.com

eBooks	Audiobooks	Fees/Services	Tours
Kindle		No	Yes

Approximate turnaround time: 1-2 mo
Where reviews are posted: Amazon, Goodreads, The Reading Room, LibraryThing
Languages: English

CATEGORIES

- **Fiction:** Contemporary, Fantasy, Science Fiction
- **Nonfiction:** Yes
- **Excluded:** Erotica, Historical Fiction

From the reviewer: I am a 20-something who loves to read. I think every book deserves to be read. However, that doesn't mean I have an infinite amount of time to do this myself. If I tell you I don't have time to read your book, it's not because I'm not interested. I just really don't have time. I love working with authors to set up guests posts or posts with book excerpts to help promote a book. Just email and ask if you have any questions.

Reviews in the City (B9-175)

http://www.reviewsinthecity.com
Andrea Jamison | ajamisonf@gmail.com

eBooks	Audiobooks	Fees/Services	Tours
Kindle, Mobi		Yes	No

Approximate turnaround time: 2-3 mo
Where reviews are posted: Inquire
Languages: English

CATEGORIES

- **Fiction:** Children's, Dystopian, Romance, Urban Fantasy
- **Nonfiction:** Yes, Biography, Self-Help
- **Excluded:** Erotica

From the reviewer: I am a writer and librarian.

BOOK BLOGGERS

Rocksprings Crafts (B9-177)

http://www.rockspringscrafts.com/book-reviews
Teresa | rockspringscrafts@gmail.com

eBooks	Audiobooks	Fees/Services	Tours
Kindle, EPUB	Yes	Inquire	No

Approximate turnaround time: 6 wk
Where reviews are posted: Amazon, Goodreads, LibraryThing, +Social
Languages: English

CATEGORIES

- **Fiction:** Crime, Literary Fiction, Science Fiction, Thriller
- **Nonfiction:** Yes, Cookbooks, Crafting, Railroad
- **Excluded:** Erotica, Religion

From the reviewer: I cannot remember a time when reading was not an important part of my life. Equally I cannot remember not wanting to share my opinions about books I love. Before the advent of the internet I kept a reading diary, I have always been a member of a reading group and love to help new authors gain a wider audience. I am happy to run Rafflecopter competitions on my blog as long as the author or promoter is willing to take responsibility for delivering any prizes.

Romancebookworm's Reviews (B9-178)

http://romancebookworm.com/
Brandy | romancebookworm@gmail.com

eBooks	Audiobooks	Fees/Services	Tours
Kindle		No	No

Approximate turnaround time: few wk
Where reviews are posted: Amazon, Goodreads, +Social
Languages: English

CATEGORIES

- **Fiction:** Mystery, Romance, Urban Fantasy
- **Nonfiction:** No
- **Excluded:** Biography, Nonfiction

From the reviewer: I'm an author myself, so I know how awkward it can be to reach out. Don't worry, I don't bite.

BOOK BLOGGERS

Roses in Ink (B9-180)

http://rosesinink.com
Jess | http://rosesinink.com/work-with-me/get-reviewed/

eBooks	Audiobooks	Fees/Services	Tours
Kindle, Mobi, PDF, DOC		Yes	Inquire

Approximate turnaround time: 1-2 mo
Where reviews are posted: Social
Languages: English

CATEGORIES

- **Fiction:** Romance
- **Nonfiction:** No
- **Excluded:** Fiction without a Romance theme, Historical Romance, Nonfiction

From the reviewer: I am a Pacific Northwest gal turned Edinburgh veterinary student. My favorite author is probably Molly McAdams, though the spot's competed for by Jennifer Armentrout and Meghan March. My goal with Roses in Ink is to create a community of communication around romance books and encourage a lifestyle of finding a rose in every day.

Sahar's Blog (B9-181)

http://www.saharsblog.com
Sahar | Use website contact form

eBooks	Audiobooks	Fees/Services	Tours
Kindle		Yes	Yes

Approximate turnaround time: Inquire
Where reviews are posted: Amazon, Goodreads, +Social
Languages: English, French

CATEGORIES

- **Fiction:** Literary Fiction, Mystery, Science Fiction, Women's Fiction
- **Nonfiction:** Yes
- **Excluded:** Erotica, Horror

From the reviewer: I am an avid reader and writer who likes to help other authors like myself trying to get the word out about their books. If you send me a print copy of your book, it will be featured on Instagram and donated to a local library to increase your visibility.

Sammy's Book Obsession (B9-182)

http://sammysbookobsession.blogspot.com/
Samantha | http://tinyurl.com/ycqsazuj

eBooks	**Audiobooks**	**Fees/Services**	**Tours**
Kindle, Mobi		Yes	Yes

Approximate turnaround time: 2 wk
Where reviews are posted: Amazon, Goodreads, BN, Kobo, Google Play Books
Languages: English

CATEGORIES

- **Fiction:** Bikers, Contemporary, Erotica, Music, NA, Romance, Sports
- **Nonfiction:** No
- **Excluded:** Dystopian, Fantasy, Historical Fiction, Horror, Nonfiction, Paranormal

From the reviewer: I'm a married, stay at home momma with a lot of free time on my hands... or I guess I WOULD have a lot of free time if I wasn't ALWAYS READING!! Love my books!! I normally read Romance, Bikers/MC (my fave), NA, Romance, Contemporary, Erotica, Sports Romance, and stuff like that. I've read SOME fantasy, but not a lot. I don't get down with the vampires, zombies, ghosts, demons (an angel here or there I can handle though), science fiction or historical stuff. I'm a blogger & reviewer and I love it!

Seeking With All Yur Heart (B9-184)

http://seekingwithallyurheart.blogspot.com
Lisa | Use website contact form

eBooks	**Audiobooks**	**Fees/Services**	**Tours**
PDF, ebooks		Inquire	No

Approximate turnaround time: 1-2 mo
Where reviews are posted: Amazon, Goodreads, LibraryThing, Books-a-Million, CD, +Social
Languages: English

CATEGORIES

- **Fiction:** Christian Fiction, Clean Romance, Mystery, Suspense, Thriller
- **Nonfiction:** Yes, Academic Books, Autobiography, Biography, Christian, Commentaries, Devotionals, Memoirs, Reference Books
- **Excluded:** Erotica, Horror, LGBTQ, Paranormal, Science Fiction

From the reviewer: I am an experienced reader, reviewer and blogger. It is the most fun thing I enjoy doing! I have used Rafflecopter and am willing to do so. The author just needs to be clear of what they desire from me.

Shari Sakurai (B9-240)

http://www.sharisakurai.com
Shari Sakurai | http://www.sharisakurai.com/reviewrequests

eBooks	Audiobooks	Fees/Services	Tours
Kindle, Mobi		No	Yes

Approximate turnaround time: Inquire
Where reviews are posted: Amazon, Goodreads, + Social
Languages: English

CATEGORIES

- **Fiction:** Dystopian, Fantasy, Horror, LGBTQ, Paranormal, Post-Apocalyptic, Science Fiction
- **Nonfiction:** No
- **Excluded:** Erotica, YA

From the reviewer: Shari Sakurai is a British author of paranormal, horror, science fiction and fantasy novels that almost always feature a LGBT protagonist and/or antagonist. She has always loved to write and it is her escape from the sometimes stressful modern life!

Aside from writing, Shari enjoys reading, watching movies, listening to (loud!) music, going to rock concerts and learning more about other societies and cultures. Japanese culture is of particular interest to her and she often incorporates Japanese themes and influences into her work.

Shari loves a challenge and has taken part and won the National Novel Writing Month challenge for the past ten years!

BOOK BLOGGERS

Sharing Life's Moments (B9-185)

http://www.sharinglifesmoments.com
Crystal Green | crystal@sharinglifesmoments.com

eBooks	Audiobooks	Fees/Services	Tours
Kindle		Yes	No

Approximate turnaround time: 3 mo
Where reviews are posted: Social
Languages: English

CATEGORIES

- **Fiction:** Most fiction considered
- **Nonfiction:** Yes
- **Excluded:** Horror

From the reviewer: I'm a work at home mom who homeschools my kids as well as blogs about our life.

She Reads New Adult (B9-186)

http://www.shereadsnewadult.com
None; use form | http://tinyurl.com/yca5lpqc

eBooks	Audiobooks	Fees/Services	Tours
Kindle		No	Yes

Approximate turnaround time: few wk
Where reviews are posted: Amazon, Goodreads, +Social
Languages: English

CATEGORIES

- **Fiction:** Dystopian, Erotica, Mystery, NA, Paranormal, Post-Apocalyptic, Romance, Suspense, YA
- **Nonfiction:** No
- **Excluded:** Comics, Historical Fiction, Nonfiction, Poetry, Religion

From the reviewer: At any given time, we have at least four ladies available to read and review multiple genres.

Shirins Book Blog and Reviews (B9-183)

http://shirinsbookblogandreviews.blogspot.in/
Shirin Rasheed | Use website contact form

eBooks	Audiobooks	Fees/Services	Tours
Kindle	Yes	Yes	Yes

Approximate turnaround time: 2-3 wk
Where reviews are posted: Amazon, Goodreads, +Social
Languages: English

CATEGORIES

- **Fiction:** Erotica, NA, Romance, YA
- **Nonfiction:** No
- **Excluded:** Comics, Nonfiction, Science Fiction

From the reviewer: I am a book lover. I love reading and promoting an author's hard work. I accept print copies for reviews as well.

Show This Book Some Love (B9-187)

https://showthisbooksomelovewordpresscom.wordpress.com/
Devon | http://showthisbooksomelove.tumblr.com/submit

eBooks	Audiobooks	Fees/Services	Tours
EPUB		No	No

Approximate turnaround time: 1-2 mo
Where reviews are posted: Amazon, Goodreads, +Social
Languages: English

CATEGORIES

- **Fiction:** Literary Fiction, Women's Fiction, YA
- **Nonfiction:** Yes, Memoirs
- **Excluded:** Biography, Christian Fiction, Erotica, Poetry

From the reviewer: I am currently about to graduate from college. My favorite books tend to be memoirs. I hope to head into the Peace Corps next September, at which point I will only accept e-books.

BOOK BLOGGERS

Simple Wyrdings (B9-188)

http://www.simplewyrdings.com
Elle | https://simplewyrdings.com/about/contact

eBooks	Audiobooks	Fees/Services	Tours
Kindle		Yes	Yes

Approximate turnaround time: 6-8 wk
Where reviews are posted: Amazon, Goodreads
Languages: English

CATEGORIES

- **Fiction:** Mystery, Romance, Science Fiction, YA
- **Nonfiction:** Yes, Self-Help
- **Excluded:** Comics, Erotica, Paranormal

From the reviewer: In my fifties. I have dogs, I raise chickens and guinea fowl, and I read. A lot.

Sleep Less, Read More (B9-189)

http://www.sleeplessreadmore.wordpress.com
EW | https://sleeplessreadmore.wordpress.com/aboutcontact/

eBooks	Audiobooks	Fees/Services	Tours
Kindle, EPUB		Yes	Yes

Approximate turnaround time: 1-2 mo
Where reviews are posted: Goodreads, +Social
Languages: English

CATEGORIES

- **Fiction:** Erotica, Fiction-General, NA
- **Nonfiction:** Yes, History, Memoirs, Sports
- **Excluded:** Action, Christian, Horror

From the reviewer: I am a freelance writer and a communicator. I usually read a book a week and I love to share my thoughts on the books I read.

So Many Books, So Little Time (B9-190)

http://www.kritikabibliophile.blogspot.com
Kritika Narula | findmereadingbooks@gmail.com

eBooks	Audiobooks	Fees/Services	Tours
Kindle, EPUB, PDF		No	Yes

Approximate turnaround time: 3 days-3 mo
Where reviews are posted: Amazon, Goodreads, Flipkart, BN, +Social
Languages: English, Hindi

CATEGORIES

- **Fiction:** Children's, Erotica, Fiction-General, Paranormal, Poetry, Romance, Science Fiction, Short Stories, YA
- **Nonfiction:** Yes, Business, Cookbooks, Management, Memoirs, Psychological, Trauma
- **Excluded:** Religion

From the reviewer: I'm a college student whose journalistic tendencies, entrepreneurial strides, and management acumen are surpassed only by her love for words. I read a lot every day, and my evolution as a person is fater than the rate at which books are being published, so I never point out to a specific genre as my favorite.

Southeast by Midwest (B9-191)

http://www.southeastbymidwest.com
Cassie or Travis | southeastbymidwestblog@gmail.com

eBooks	Audiobooks	Fees/Services	Tours
EPUB	Yes	No	No

Approximate turnaround time: 4 wk
Where reviews are posted: Amazon, Goodreads, +Social
Languages: English

CATEGORIES

- **Fiction:** Cozy Mystery, Paranormal, Romance, Science Fiction, YA
- **Nonfiction:** Yes, Biography, Cookbooks, Memoirs, Self-Help
- **Excluded:** Erotica, Horror, Romance

From the reviewer: I am a beauty blogger who also likes to blog about the other beautiful things in life.

Stephanie's Book Reports (B9-192)

http://www.stephaniesbookreports.com

Stephanie | http://www.stephaniesbookreports.com/review-request

eBooks	Audiobooks	Fees/Services	Tours
Kindle	Yes	Yes	Yes

Approximate turnaround time: ~1 mo

Where reviews are posted: Amazon, Goodreads, +Social

Languages: English

CATEGORIES

- **Fiction:** Romance, NA, YA
- **Nonfiction:** No
- **Excluded:** Biography, Comics, Nonfiction

From the reviewer: I am a stay-at-home mom who loves to read. I started my blog to help readers find the books they're looking for. Stephanie's Book Reports strives to review as many books in a month as possible. Reviewers mostly take e-books, but they also will take galley and audiobooks for review as well.

Succotash Book Reviews (B9-193)

http://succotashreviews.blogspot.com
Renee Shelton | sandandsuccotash@gmail.com

eBooks	Audiobooks	Fees/Services	Tours
No		Inquire	Yes

Approximate turnaround time: Inquire
Where reviews are posted: Amazon, Goodreads, BN, Smashwords, LibraryThing, +Social
Languages: English

CATEGORIES

- **Fiction:** Chick Lit, Crime, Humor, Mystery, Politics, Romance
- **Nonfiction:** Yes, Cookbooks, Crafting, Fishing, Food, Jewelry Making, Reference, Sewing
- **Excluded:** Children's, Horror, Supernatural Extreme

From the reviewer: I run my own home based business, and manage 10 different niche blogs. Between my business and being an active mom, my favorite pastime is reading. My hobby of reading has grown into working with indie authors, publishers, and publicists reading and reviewing books. While the types of books I read for this blog are already listed, if you have a genre that I have not reviewed in a while, make a good pitch to get me interested. I read a wide range of books, and if you self-publish show me that you believe in your book. I believe every story is worth reading. I just wish I had the time to read them all.

BOOK BLOGGERS

Teatime and Books (B9-195)

http://www.teatimeandbooks76.blogspot.com
Janet | empointeediting@gmail.com

eBooks	Audiobooks	Fees/Services	Tours
Kindle		Yes	Yes

Approximate turnaround time: 2-3 wk
Where reviews are posted: Amazon, Goodreads, Kobo, BN, +Social
Languages: English

CATEGORIES

- **Fiction:** Children's, Clean Romance, Contemporary, Cozy Mystery, Historical Fiction, Historical Romance, Mystery, Suspense, YA
- **Nonfiction:** Yes, Devotionals, Educational, History, Medical, Memoirs
- **Excluded:** Erotica, Horror, Science Fiction

From the reviewer: I am a teacher, author assistant and book editor. I'm also an avid reader and a huge fan of historical romance, cozy mysteries and a good thriller and suspense.

The Audiobookworm (B9-196)

http://theaudiobookworm.com/
Jess | http://theaudiobookworm.com/requests/

eBooks	Audiobooks	Fees/Services	Tours
No	Yes	Yes	Yes

Approximate turnaround time: 1 mo
Where reviews are posted: Goodreads, Audible, +Social
Languages: English

CATEGORIES

- **Fiction:** Contemporary, Fiction-General, Historical Fiction, NA, Romance, Suspense, Thriller, YA
- **Nonfiction:** No
- **Excluded:** Children's, Erotica, Horror, Middle Grade, Nonfiction, Religion

From the reviewer: The Audiobookworm is an audiobook review blog and is one of only a few on the web that reviews audiobooks exclusively.

The Book Binder's Daughter (B9-198)

http://www.thebookbindersdaughter.com
Melissa Beck | magistrabeck@outlook.com

eBooks	Audiobooks	Fees/Services	Tours
Kindle		No	Yes

Approximate turnaround time: 3-4 mo
Where reviews are posted: Amazon, Goodreads, LibraryThing, +Social
Languages: English

CATEGORIES

- **Fiction:** Classics, Historical Fiction, Literary Fiction, Poetry
- **Nonfiction:** Yes, Cookbooks, History, Travel
- **Excluded:** Dystopian, Erotica, Science Fiction, YA

From the reviewer: I am a Latin and ancient Greek teacher who loves to read serious literary fiction and classics.

The Book Cove (B9-199)

http://www.thebookcove.com
Jessi | http://www.thebookcove.com/p/about-cove.html

eBooks	Audiobooks	Fees/Services	Tours
Kindle		No	Yes

Approximate turnaround time: 2 mo
Where reviews are posted: Amazon, Goodreads, +Social
Languages: English

CATEGORIES

- **Fiction:** Erotica, NA, Paranormal, Romance
- **Nonfiction:** No
- **Excluded:** Science Fiction, YA

From the reviewer: I am a graduate student who reviews book in any free time. I love almost all genres, but choose to review only a few of those, including paranormal romance, new adult romance, and suspense.

The Book Disciple (B9-200)

http://www.thebookdisciple.com
Samantha | Use website contact form

eBooks	Audiobooks	Fees/Services	Tours
Kindle	Yes	No	Yes

Approximate turnaround time: 2-3 mo
Where reviews are posted: Amazon, Goodreads, +Social
Languages: English

CATEGORIES

- **Fiction:** Contemporary Romance, Historical Fiction, NA, Paranormal, Romance, Suspense
- **Nonfiction:** Yes, True Crime
- **Excluded:** Erotica, Horror, YA

From the reviewer: I am a special education teacher who loves romance in all its sub-genres!

The Cosy Dragon (B9-204)

http://www.thecosydragon.com
Rosemarie Herbert | thecosydragon@gmail.com

eBooks	Audiobooks	Fees/Services	Tours
No		Yes	No

Approximate turnaround time: 2-3 mo
Where reviews are posted: Amazon, Goodreads, +Social
Languages: English

CATEGORIES

- **Fiction:** Action, Children's, Crime, Erotica, Fantasy, Fiction-General, LGBTQ, Middle Grade, Romance, Thriller, Women's Fiction, YA
- **Nonfiction:** Yes, Cookbooks, Crafting, Gardening, Memoirs, Self-Help, True Crime
- **Excluded:** Christian, Comics, Graphic, Poetry, Short Stories

From the reviewer: I'm an Australian blogger who lives in Melbourne, Victoria. I don't have any pets, vices (apart from books), and am committed to life-long education. With this in mind, my official qualifications are a BA in Literature and Religious studies and a BS/BBS in Biochemistry and Genetics (H1 Honours). I am currently undertaking a PhD in Genetics at Monash University. I started this blog way back in 2012 because I wasn't reading all of the novels I was buying. Four years on, I hardly ever buy books, and receive most of my reading material from publishers and indie authors. I also enjoy the occasional talking book borrowed from my local library.

BOOK BLOGGERS

The Howling Turtle (B9-205)

http://howlingturtle-pdx.blogspot.com
Larissa | howlingturtle19@gmail.com

eBooks	Audiobooks	Fees/Services	Tours
Kindle, Mobi, PDF, EPUB	Yes	Yes	Yes

Approximate turnaround time: several mo
Where reviews are posted: Amazon, Goodreads, +Social
Languages: English

CATEGORIES

• **Fiction:** Fantasy, LGBTQ, Romance, Science Fiction
• **Nonfiction:** No
• **Excluded:** Christian, Horror, Nonfiction

From the reviewer: I am currently a college student at St. Olaf double majoring in English (surprise) and Women and Gender Studies. On top of being a complete bookworm I am also an avid handcrafted and love to knit, crochet, and bead.

The Phantom Paragrapher (B9-207)

http://www.thephantomparagrapher.blogspot.com
Paula | paulazone@live.com

eBooks	Audiobooks	Fees/Services	Tours
Kindle, EPUB, PDF		Inquire	Yes

Approximate turnaround time: 3-6 mo
Where reviews are posted: Amazon, Goodreads, ChicklitClub
Languages: English

CATEGORIES

• **Fiction:** Most fiction considered
• **Nonfiction:** Yes
• **Excluded:** Erotica

From the reviewer: Lifestyle Editor for Paper Droids. She is a self-proclaimed geek chic She also can be found at her version of The Daily Planet—The Phantom Paragrapher.

The Reading Life (B9-208)

http://rereadinglives.blogspot.com
Mel U. | rereadinglives@gmail.com

eBooks	Audiobooks	Fees/Services	Tours
Kindle		Inquire	No

Approximate turnaround time: 1-2 mo
Where reviews are posted: Amazon, +Social
Languages: English

CATEGORIES

- **Fiction:** Contemporary, Literary Fiction, Irish Literature, Post-Colonial Asian Fiction
- **Nonfiction:** Yes, Biography, History
- **Excluded:** Christian, Comics

From the reviewer: I have been an avid reader for over fifty years.

The Rebel Christian (B9-209)

http://www.therebelchristian.com
Vee Garris | http://www.therebelchristian.com/new-page/

eBooks	Audiobooks	Fees/Services	Tours
Mobi, EPUB, PDF		Yes	Yes

Approximate turnaround time: 1 mo
Where reviews are posted: Amazon, Goodreads
Languages: English

CATEGORIES

- **Fiction:** Christian Fiction, Contemporary, Paranormal, Science Fiction, YA
- **Nonfiction:** No
- **Excluded:** Erotica, Historical Fiction, LGBTQ, Nonfiction, Poetry, Time Travel, Western

From the reviewer: I am a loving Christian and an avid reader with a passion for writing. I have a Bachelors in Psychology from Medaille College and I'm certified in Copy Editing by Poynter. News University. As a self-published author, I love helping others in my field. I specialize in working with new and indie authors by providing quality reviews and other editorial services. The Rebel Christian is the love of my life! I greatly enjoy running it because--like my books--it's all mine!

BOOK BLOGGERS

The Romance Cover (B9-210)

http://www.theromancecover.com/
Donna | theromancecover@gmail.com

eBooks	Audiobooks	Fees/Services	Tours
Kindle		No	No

Approximate turnaround time: 1-2 mo
Where reviews are posted: Amazon, Goodreads, +Social
Languages: English

CATEGORIES

- **Fiction:** Contemporary Romance, Erotica, Mystery, NA, Paranormal, Romance, Suspense, YA
- **Nonfiction:** No
- **Excluded:** Biography, Comics, Historical Fiction, Nonfiction

From the reviewer: Our information can be found on our about page.

The Serial Reader Blog (B9-211)

http://theserialreaderblog.com
Scila | http://theserialreaderblog.com/review-request-policy

eBooks	Audiobooks	Fees/Services	Tours
Kindle, Mobi		Yes	Yes

Approximate turnaround time: 1 mo
Where reviews are posted: Amazon, Goodreads, MTS.com, +Social
Languages: English, Spanish, Italian

CATEGORIES

- **Fiction:** Fantasy, Fiction-General, Horror, Humor, Literary Fiction, Mystery, NA, Science Fiction, Thriller, YA
- **Nonfiction:** Yes
- **Excluded:** Erotica

From the reviewer: I am an avid reader, freelance writer and student.

The Violent Vixen (B9-212)

http://theviolentvixen.blogspot.com
Courtney | solacecai@gmail.com

eBooks	Audiobooks	Fees/Services	Tours
Mobi, EPUB		Yes	Yes

Approximate turnaround time: 1-3 mo
Where reviews are posted: Amazon, Goodreads, NetGalley, +Social
Languages: English

CATEGORIES

- **Fiction:** Dystopian, Fantasy, Fiction-General, Horror, Paranormal, Romance, Thriller
- **Nonfiction:** No
- **Excluded:** Nonfiction, Poetry, Violence

From the reviewer: I am a wife and mom. I love to read a fairly diverse collection of books. I often call myself the "devourer of books" because I read so much.

TicToc Reviews (B9-213)

http://www.wrighton-time.blogspot.com/
Leslie Wright | lesliewrightauthor@gmail.com

eBooks	Audiobooks	Fees/Services	Tours
No		No	Yes

Approximate turnaround time: 1-2 mo
Where reviews are posted: Amazon, Goodreads, Blogcritics, +Social
Languages: English

CATEGORIES

- **Fiction:** Dystopian, Historical Fiction, Mystery, Paranormal, Romance, Science Fiction, Thriller, YA
- **Nonfiction:** Yes
- **Excluded:** Erotica, Poetry

From the reviewer: I work a full-time job at a minimum of fifty-five hours a week, but I also write books and review books for others.

Tiffany's Book Blog (B9-214)

http://www.tiffanysbookblog.com
Tiffany | engler.tiffany@gmail.com

eBooks	Audiobooks	Fees/Services	Tours
No		No	Yes

Approximate turnaround time: 1-2 mo
Where reviews are posted: Amazon, Goodreads, BN
Languages: English

CATEGORIES

- **Fiction:** Contemporary, Erotica, LGBTQ, NA, Romance, YA
- **Nonfiction:** Yes, Cookbooks, Crafting, Writing
- **Excluded:** Biography, Christian, Comics

From the reviewer: I am a mom who just loves to read! I love posting reviews as I feel like it helps encourages authors to continue their awesome works!

To Be A Person (B9-215)

http://mautobeaperson.com
Miranda A. Uyeh | http://mautobeaperson.com/contact

eBooks	Audiobooks	Fees/Services	Tours
Kindle, EPUB, PDF		No	No

Approximate turnaround time: 3 mo
Where reviews are posted: Amazon, Goodreads, +Social
Languages: English

CATEGORIES

- **Fiction:** Christian Fiction
- **Nonfiction:** Yes, Devotionals, Memoirs, Self-Help
- **Excluded:** Erotica, Horror, LGBTQ

From the reviewer: I'm the editor of TBAP, a website that celebrates inspirational lifestyle, literature and entertainment. I'm the author of To Die Once: Child of Grace, #1, and a Mogul Global Ambassador. I was shortlisted in 2014 to be a judge in the Inspy Awards for the category Contemporary Romance/Romance-suspense. I'm presently writing To Lie Once, the sequel to To Die Once. You can connect with me on my website, Twitter or Facebook.

Twinsie Talk Book Reviews (B9-217)

http://www.twinsietalk.com
Angie, Melinda, Kristi, Kelly, Brenda, Jo, Jen and Deb
Twinsies@TwinsieTalk.com

BOOK BLOGGERS

eBooks	Audiobooks	Fees/Services	Tours
Kindle, Nook		Yes	Yes

Approximate turnaround time: 1 mo
Where reviews are posted: Amazon, Goodreads, +Social
Languages: English

CATEGORIES

• **Fiction:** Apocalyptic, Contemporary, Historical Romance, LGBTQ, NA, Paranormal, Romance, Urban Fiction, YA
• **Nonfiction:** No
• **Excluded:** Horror, Non-Romance

From the reviewer: We are all full-time employees who use reading to escape.

Up 'Til Dawn Book Blog (B9-218)

http://uptildawnbookblog.blogspot.com
Dawn West | http://tinyurl.com/yaz428u7

eBooks	Audiobooks	Fees/Services	Tours
Mobi, EPUB, PDF	Yes	Yes	Yes

Approximate turnaround time: 1 mo
Where reviews are posted: Amazon, Goodreads
Languages: English

CATEGORIES

- **Fiction:** Contemporary Romance, Erotica, Fantasy, Historical Romance, NA, Paranormal, Romance, Science Fiction, Women's Fiction, YA
- **Nonfiction:** No
- **Excluded:** Horror, Nonfiction, Nonfiction, Poetry, (fiction without a romance theme is not accepted)

From the reviewer: I'm a 30-year-old book devourer with a love of Double Stuff Oreos and the Sims! On the Up 'Til Dawr. Book Blog, I post mainly spoiler-free reviews sprinkled with quirky gifs and graphics. All reviews are simultaneously posted to my Goodreads profile. I participate in blog tours through several fabulous tour companies, as well as review via NetGalley, Edelweiss, The Romance Reviews, Reading Alley, and directly through publishing and book publicity companies.

Urban Book Reviews (B9-219)

https://urbanbookreviewsrus.wordpress.com
Danielle Urban | http://tinyurl.com/ybsaksgu

eBooks	Audiobooks	Fees/Services	Tours
Kindle, Mobi, PDF		Yes	Yes

Approximate turnaround time: 1-3 mo
Where reviews are posted: Amazon, Goodreads, +Social
Languages: English

CATEGORIES

- **Fiction:** Most fiction considered
- **Nonfiction:** Yes, Business, Cookbooks, Crafting, Educational, Memoirs, Self-Help
- **Excluded:** Erotica

From the reviewer: I am a college student finishing up my second college degree. Only 6 more classes left to go. I have interned as an editor, book reviewer, and article writer with several companies online. I am still a writer for The Typewriter. This organization is an international news organization that I have belonged to for the past two years. I am still with them. Plus, I belong to several author street teams including Brenda Novak, Samantha Chase, Nicole Strycharz and many others.

Urban Smoothie Read (B9-220)

http://www.urbansmoothie.com
Amanda Lee | paccodemongrel@gmail.com

eBooks	Audiobooks	Fees/Services	Tours
Kindle		Yes	Yes

Approximate turnaround time: 1 wk
Where reviews are posted: Amazon, Goodreads
Languages: English

CATEGORIES

- **Fiction:** Erotica, Romance
- **Nonfiction:** No
- **Excluded:** Biography, Christian, YA

From the reviewer: I love reading romance especially dark and dirty.

Walking on Bookshelves (B9-221)

http://www.walkingonbookshelves.blogspot.com
Jeannette | http://tinyurl.com/ybuxpmcb

eBooks	Audiobooks	Fees/Services	Tours
Kindle		No	No

Approximate turnaround time: 2-4 wk
Where reviews are posted: Amazon, Goodreads, +Social
Languages: English

CATEGORIES

- **Fiction:** Chick Lit, Clean Romance, Fantasy, Paranormal, Romance, YA
- **Nonfiction:** No
- **Excluded:** Erotica, Horror, Nonfiction

From the reviewer: I am so grateful when an author gives me the privilege to review their book. It takes great courage and heart to allow total strangers to critique a piece of you. I am always honest, even if I have to give a bad review. Reviews are just opinions and there as many opinions as there are people. So, I'm just one voice in a chorus. I will do spotlight posts & giveaways. Just ask!!

What's Beyond Forks? (B9-222)

http://www.whatsbeyondforks.com
Gabby | http://www.whatsbeyondforks.com/p/contact-me.html

eBooks	Audiobooks	Fees/Services	Tours
EPUB, PDF		No	Yes

Approximate turnaround time: Inquire
Where reviews are posted: Amazon, Goodreads, BN, +Social
Languages: English

CATEGORIES

- **Fiction:** Christian Fiction, Contemporary Romance, Dystopian, NA, Paranormal, YA
- **Nonfiction:** No
- **Excluded:** Nonfiction

From the reviewer: I enjoy reading fiction of all kinds, and I love sharing what I read with others, so here I am.

Wishful Endings (B9-224)

http://www.wishfulendings.com/
Tressa | wishfulendings@outlook.com

eBooks	Audiobooks	Fees/Services	Tours
Kindle, PDF		Yes	Yes

Approximate turnaround time: 3 mo
Where reviews are posted: Amazon, Goodreads, BN, +Social
Languages: English

CATEGORIES

- **Fiction:** Children's, Christian Romance, Clean Romance, YA
- **Nonfiction:** Yes, Cookbooks, Crafting, Gardening, Hobby Titles, Interior Design, Movies, Music Albums, Sewing
- **Excluded:** Erotica, Horror

From the reviewer: I am a stay-at-home happily married mom who has loved to read since I was a child. I love young adult books and clean romance the most! I can run a giveaway or another promotional post if the book meets my criteria and I'm unable to review. Please ask if interested in me doing so.

Women Connect Online (B9-225)

http://womenconnectonline.com
Yvonne W | http://womenconnectonline.com/review-policy

eBooks	Audiobooks	Fees/Services	Tours
Yes		Yes	Yes

Approximate turnaround time: 2 mo
Where reviews are posted: Amazon, Goodreads, +Social
Languages: English

CATEGORIES

- **Fiction:** Fiction-General
- **Nonfiction:** Yes
- **Excluded:** Children's, Erotica, History

From the reviewer: Created a site devoted to meeting the needs of women. I like to participate in blog tours and will post contests on my site.

BOOK BLOGGERS

Words and Peace (B9-226)

http://wordsandpeace.com
Emma | https://wordsandpeace.com/contact-me/

eBooks	Audiobooks	Fees/Services	Tours
Kindle, Mobi, EPUB	Yes	No	Yes

Approximate turnaround time: 1 mo
Where reviews are posted: Amazon, Goodreads, BN, +Social
Languages: English, French

CATEGORIES
- **Fiction:** Historical Fiction, Literary Fiction, Mystery
- **Nonfiction:** Yes, Biography, History, Literary Criticism, Spirituality, Theology
- **Excluded:** Erotica, Horror, Paranormal, Romance, Sports, YA

From the reviewer: I am a translator and language teacher.

Writing Pearls (B9-227)

http://www.writingpearls.com
Jessica Samuelsen | http://writingpearls.com/contact-us

eBooks	Audiobooks	Fees/Services	Tours
Kindle		No	Yes

Approximate turnaround time: 1-2 mo
Where reviews are posted: Amazon, Goodreads, +Social
Languages: English

CATEGORIES
- **Fiction:** Chick Lit, Clean Romance, Cozy Mystery, Women's Fiction, YA
- **Nonfiction:** No
- **Excluded:** Erotica, Horror, Nonfiction

From the reviewer: I am a life-long reader who is always on the hunt for a quality book. I have published The Wake of 30 in my crazy poetry days. I am now working on my debut novel set to come out sometime next year. I work for Sprkit as a professional reviewer.

Zapkode Marie (B9-228)

http://www.zapkodemarie.net
Annie | I.heart.books.831@gmail.com

eBooks	Audiobooks	Fees/Services	Tours
Mobi, EPUB		No	No

Approximate turnaround time: ASAP
Where reviews are posted: Amazon, Goodreads, +Social
Languages: English

CATEGORIES

- **Fiction:** Children's, Middle Grade, YA
- **Nonfiction:** Yes, Children's, Middle Grade, YA
- **Excluded:** Erotica

From the reviewer: I am 33 years old and married to Mel. Combined we have three kidlets: Cheya (age: 13), Riley (age: 12), Austin (age: 10) & Emma (9 months). I also have 3 cats (Sugar, Giggles & Abby), 2 dogs (Libby & Kaydee). We also have a rat (Raven). I have obtained my AA in (Informational Technology and Visual Communications) and my BA in (Criminal Justice). I changed majors mainly because I did not feel as if I was being challenged. I have a number of interests such as: reading, digital scrapbooking, photography, video games, computer games and spending my time with my kidlets.

BOOK BLOGGERS

Zili in the Sky (B9-229)

http://www.ziliinthesky.com/
Zili Robins | zilirobins@gmail.com

eBooks	Audiobooks	Fees/Services	Tours
Kindle		Yes	Yes

Approximate turnaround time: Inquire
Where reviews are posted: Amazon, Goodreads, +Social
Languages: English

CATEGORIES

• **Fiction:** NA, Paranormal, Urban Fantasy, YA
• **Nonfiction:** No
• **Excluded:** Dark Romance, Erotica, Nonfiction, Religious Fiction

From the reviewer: I have a M.A. in English and English literature. I'm based in England, but work with lots of authors, PRs, and publishers all around the world. I run lots giveaways and I am always happy to take part in tours, promotions, and cover reveals.

Part 2
Blog Tour
Organizers

Introduction

All the services profiled in this section help organize book blog tours on behalf of authors. So instead of the author contacting each of the book bloggers profiled in Part 1, tour organizers do it for them. This has several advantages:

1. Most importantly, this saves authors (or publishers) time. Instead of manually combing through pages to find the perfect reviewers, these firms often have relationships with lots of bloggers.

2. Equally important, the book bloggers that signup have voluntarily asked to be contacted by these tour organizers. They've opted in.

3. Because they have these relationships, they can often deliver results more quickly. Authors who have tight timelines should get better results.

4. Most do more than organize a tour. Related services can include cover reveals, release day blitzes, and social media blitzes. Many also offer other public relations (PR) services such as managing FaceBook advertising as well as social media outreach and training. A few even offer editorial and graphic design services.

5. Finally, if this is your first book you're likely overwhelmed by the number of tasks you can or should do. For a relatively small investment you can get a time-consuming task done for you, and learn something in the process for next time.

TERMINOLOGY

Blog Tours. Like a traditional book tour, but virtual, authors go from blog to blog to create publicity for their book and themselves. These are pre-arranged events and authors participate in a variety of ways such as providing a written interview, an article, a giveaway, an excerpt, a new book cover—or combinations of these.

Tour Organizer. An individual or firm that organizes blog tours for authors. Organizing tours is often one of several services, not the sole service.

Tour Host, or simply **Host.** A blogger, such as those listed in Part 1.

Tour Stop. Each tour makes use of several tour hosts. When the tour host adds a post or promotes the author's book, that's called a tour stop.

Blitz or Blast. No standardized meaning. We use it to refer to short promotions, as in one-time, where there is no follow up or monitoring of the people that receive the blast/blitz. It can sometimes be booked with less notice than a tour. Some of these tour organizers use the term to describe a multi-day tour but we consider this to be an oxymoron.

PR Friendly. The website accepts some type of paid advertising.

Guest Blogging. In this context it is an article written by the author for someone else's blog.

WHAT YOU GIVE UP

With few exceptions, their services are not free. However, entry-level costs for a basic tour usually range from $25 to $150. Be sure to read the fine print; prices do change. A listing here does not mean these firms will accept your book, nor have we vetted their services.

Their services are more like a shotgun than a rifle. If your book has a special angle, or appeals to a select audience, these firms may not be a match. To make their business work at the prices they charge, they can't necessarily guarantee your book will be reviewed or promoted by specific blogs.

Perhaps most importantly, you don't have as much control or knowledge about who is writing reviews, or how the reviews are promoted. This only comes from hand-picking bloggers who you want to review your book.

HOW TO USE

Begin by recognizing that the services offered by these firms are not solely focused on reviews, they are broadly promotional in nature. Here are a few different ways to use the firms and services in this section:

For a release weeks or months in advance. In this case you are most likely focused on reviews. Most, not all, have services to help you reach bloggers with advance reading copies of your book. Many accept PDF and eBook formats. Look for services that specifically mention reviews or include reviews.

Promotions on and around release day. All these firms offer at least one service that promotes books close to or soon after release date. These are interview opportunities, guest post opportunities, giveaways, spotlights, and teaser content. The price shown in the listing is the lowest price for their book review tour service. These services are often listed as "Tours."

Reboots and periodic sales for previously released books. A number offer "blitz" and "blast" services where information about your book's sale price or special offer is emailed out to their list of bloggers. Many of these can be done on short notice, and may be repeated as needed.

Specialty services. While most if not all promote genre fiction, there are a few that specialize (for example, *The Audiobookworm* for audio book promotions, *Lone Star Literary Life* for books related to Texas, and *Italy Book Tours* for books with an Italian theme). This is a trend we hope to see more of.

Author/book services. Many of the services here are offered by individuals, a few by small teams, a couple are larger book marketing firms with a staff. What sets them apart is that they all love books. They see scores of books every week and have lots of publishing relationships.

Some put their passions, skills, and relationships to work in related publishing areas as diverse as website design, editing, and creating book trailers. If you find someone you trust and enjoy working with, find out what other things they can help you with.

Avoid scheduling overlapping promotions

Book bloggers (also known as tour hosts) often work with several tour organizers. If you submit your book to two or more tour organizers for the same time period you may find the same book blogger (tour host) listed on more than one tour schedule. This means you are getting fewer overall posts about your book and less promotion.

Many tour organizers ask you to not do this because it gets confusing for everyone involved. Plus, it hurts their chances of delivering what you paid for, which creates ill feelings for everyone involved.

Our advice: Find a tour organizer you want to use and book your promotion. Wait three to four weeks after it ends to book a tour with another organizer.

Less than flattering reviews

Tour hosts are often asked by tour organizers to **not** post reviews on their blog during the tour dates if the review is lower than a specified level, such as three (out of five) stars. They ask them to hold the review until after the tour concludes. Book bloggers as a group view their opinion as just that, an opinion, something the author can't buy.

A typical statement on the tour organizer's pricing page is something like: "Host reviews under 3.5 stars will not be posted during the tour, but may be posted after the tour at the host's discretion."

As the author, the way to mitigate this is to write a great book and produce it in a professional manner. Beyond this, it's up to the reader to decide if they like it. And if a reviewer doesn't like a book, it doesn't mean the review is "bad," it just wasn't for them.

Just keep in mind that they cannot guarantee a tour host will comply.

Tour Organizer Listing Key

Information, pricing, and services are subject to change without notice. Always review the website information and policies before contacting a Tour Organizer. A listing here does not mean your book will be accepted.

 Use this code when reporting errors or updates for this specific listing via the GIVE updates link in the footer.

 Tour organizers can offer several services. This link takes you to their blog tour organizer information.

 Special Focus: A few specialize in narrow categories, such as a specific country, or a state.

 Affiliate(s): Organizers may have more than one website, or a relationship with another entity. If so, that is noted here.

 Starting $: The lowest price charged to organize a blog tour for reviews. Note that prices and services are subject to change.

 Blast/Blitz: Whether they offer this service, or not (see terminology).

 Marketing: Services can include training, social media support, event organizing, advertising placement, website development, and related.

 VA/PA: Virtual assistant/personal assistant services.

 Publishing: Services can include designing book covers, editing, proofing, eBook programming, and related.

 Categories: Tour organizers are usually less specialized than book bloggers in terms of what categories of books they accept. However, those that indicate specific specialties or exclusions are noted here. Always confirm with the organizer whether he or she can promote your book.

Enchanted Book Promotions (T9-002) ←

http://www.enchantedbookpromotions.com/
Tour Information: http://tinyurl.com/y7b8p48g ←
Special Focus: ←
Affiliation(s): ←

Starting $	Blast/Blitz	Marketing	VA/PA	Publishing
$35	Yes	Yes		Yes

CATEGORIES

• **Fiction:** All including erotica
• **Nonfiction:**
• **Excluded:**

About: Enchanted Book Promotions has been helping authors and promoting books since 2011. We offer various services, ranging from virtual book tours to marketing services such as writing a professional press release, setting up a newsletter for your website, managing your social media and organizing a custom book marketing campaign for your novel. We also offer webdesign services.

Ardent Prose (T9-031)

http://ardentprose.com/
Tour Information: http://ardentprose.com/contact-me/
Special Focus: N/A
Affiliation(s): N/A

Starting $	Blast/Blitz	Marketing	VA/PA	Publishing
Inquire		Yes	Yes	

CATEGORIES

- **Fiction:** Inquire
- **Nonfiction:**
- **Excluded:**

About: Ardent Prose offers a number of author services in addition to organizing blog tours: editorial support, social media marketing, and coordinating promotions and advertising, to name a few.

b00k r3vi3w Tours (T9-014)

http://www.b00kr3vi3ws.in/
Tour Information: http://www.b00kr3vi3ws.in/p/services.html
Special Focus: N/A
Affiliation(s): N/A

Starting $	Blast/Blitz	Marketing	VA/PA	Publishing
Inquire	Yes		Yes	

CATEGORIES

- **Fiction:** Contemporary, Fantasy, Mystery, NA, Paranormal, Romance, Thriller, YA
- **Nonfiction:**
- **Excluded:** Erotica, Nonfiction

About: My name is Debdatta Dasgupta Sahay and I am a book addict from India. When I am not reading, I am driving people nuts by talking about them. I used to be a Human Resource Professional with 6 years of work experience under my belt. I am currently pursuing my 2nd Post-Graduate degree in Mass Communication and Journalism. I started b00k r3vi3ws blog back in February, 2012 as an outlet for my bookish craziness. I also started b00k r3vi3w Tours in October 2014 to help promote books.

TOUR ORGANIZERS

Beck Valley Books (T9-015)

http://beckvalleybooks.blogspot.com
Tour Information: http://tinyurl.com/yct4pomr
Special Focus: N/A
Affiliation(s): N/A

Starting $	Blast/Blitz	Marketing	VA/PA	Publishing
Inquire	Yes			

CATEGORIES

- **Fiction:** Children's, Crime, Fantasy, General Fiction, General Nonfiction, Memoirs, Mystery, Romance, Self-Help, Suspense, Thriller, YA
- **Nonfiction:**
- **Excluded:** None

About: I'm a mum of two teenagers, who has built up the tour company from 2008 to its recommended service it is today.

Bewitching Book Tours (T9-001)

http://www.bewitchingbooktours.com/
Tour Information: http://tinyurl.com/y7zqqbbc
Special Focus: N/A
Affiliation(s): N/A

Starting $	Blast/Blitz	Marketing	VA/PA	Publishing
$45	Yes	Yes		

CATEGORIES

- **Fiction:** All including erotica
- **Nonfiction:**
- **Excluded:** Christian

About: Bewitching Book Tours is geared towards the new author, the eBook author, the small and independent press author, and the mid-list author- the author who doesn't have a huge marketing budget but wants the most bang for their promotional buck.

Buoni Amici Press (T9-033)

http://buoniamicipress.com/
Tour Information: http://buoniamicipress.com/author-services/
Special Focus: N/A
Affiliation(s): N/A

Starting $	Blast/Blitz	Marketing	VA/PA	Publishing
$80		Yes		

CATEGORIES

- **Fiction:** Inquire
- **Nonfiction:**
- **Excluded:**

About: Buoni Amici Press is a team of three people offering authors offering book marketing, promotions and design services.

Celebrate Lit Publicity Group (T9-016)

http://www.celebratelit.com
Tour Information: http://www.celebratelit.com/19-2/
Special Focus: N/A
Affiliation(s): N/A

Starting $	Blast/Blitz	Marketing	VA/PA	Publishing
Inquire				

CATEGORIES

- **Fiction:** Christian Fiction, Christian Nonfiction
- **Nonfiction:** Christian Nonfiction
- **Excluded:** Non-Christian

About: We run Celebrate Lit as a ministry to help great Christian authors get their books into the hands of wonderful readers!

TOUR ORGANIZERS

Electively Paige (T9-034)

http://electivelypaige.com/
Tour Information: http://electivelypaige.com/blog-tours/
Special Focus: N/A
Affiliation(s): N/A

Starting $	Blast/Blitz	Marketing	VA/PA	Publishing
$60	Yes			

CATEGORIES
- **Fiction:** Inquire
- **Nonfiction:**
- **Excluded:**

About: See listing in Book Bloggers.

TOUR ORGANIZERS

Enchanted Book Promotions (T9-002)

http://www.enchantedbookpromotions.com/
Tour Information: http://tinyurl.com/y7b8p48g
Special Focus: N/A
Affiliation(s): N/A

Starting $	Blast/Blitz	Marketing	VA/PA	Publishing
$35	Yes	Yes		Yes

CATEGORIES
- **Fiction:** All including erotica
- **Nonfiction:**
- **Excluded:**

About: Enchanted Book Promotions has been helping authors and promoting books since 2011. We offer various services, ranging from virtual book tours to marketing services such as writing a professional press release, setting up a newsletter for your website, managing your social media and organizing a custom book marketing campaign for your novel. We also offer webdesign services.

Fantastic Flying Book Club (T9-035)

http://fantasticflyingbookclub.blogspot.com/
Tour Information: http://tinyurl.com/y82g9g7l
Special Focus: N/A
Affiliation(s): N/A

Starting $	Blast/Blitz	Marketing	VA/PA	Publishing
$0				

CATEGORIES

- **Fiction:** Inquire
- **Nonfiction:**
- **Excluded:**

About: The two-person team behind the Fantastic Flying Book Club is a rarity in these listings: their tours are offered free of charge. Each month they host at least one blog tour to celebrate the release of a book.

France Book Tours (T9-017)

http://francebooktours.com
Tour Information: https://francebooktours.com/author-application/
Special Focus: France: books with a connection to France.
Affiliation(s): N/A

Starting $	Blast/Blitz	Marketing	VA/PA	Publishing
$45				Yes

CATEGORIES

- **Fiction:** Fiction, France, Mystery, Nonfiction
- **Nonfiction:** France
- **Excluded:** Erotica

About: France Book Tours was the first virtual book tour company dedicated to a specific country.

TOUR ORGANIZERS

Goddess Fish Promotions (T9-003)

http://www.goddessfish.com/
Tour Information: http://www.
goddessfish.com/services/
Special Focus: N/A
Affiliation(s): N/A

Starting $	Blast/Blitz	Marketing	VA/PA	Publishing
$55		Yes		Yes

CATEGORIES

- **Fiction:** Middle Grade, Mystery, Fantasy, Romance (all sub-genres), Science Fiction, YA
- **Nonfiction:**
- **Excluded:** Poetry

About: Goddess Fish Promotions was established November 14, 2008. Why? Well, when Marianne became a published author and got her the first taste of trying to promote a book on a budget, there was only one other virtual book tour company in place at the time, and their fees were simply too high for a small press author. After coordinating and running her own tour, she knew other authors could use the same service for a reasonable price. Thus, Goddess Fish Promotions was born.

TOUR ORGANIZERS

I Am A Reader (T9-018)

http://iamareader.com
Tour Information: http://www.iamareader.com/blast-tour-pricing
Special Focus: N/A
Affiliation(s): N/A

Starting $	Blast/Blitz	Marketing	VA/PA	Publishing
$125	Yes			

CATEGORIES

- **Fiction:** Clean Romance, Family-Friendly, YA
- **Nonfiction:**
- **Excluded:** Erotica, Horror, Steamy Romance

About: I host tours and blasts on iamareader.com I also have a site e-Booksforreview.com where I get books into the hands of readers who post on Amazon & Goodreads.

IndieSage PR (T9-004)

http://indiesage.com/
Tour Information: http://indiesage.com/services/
Special Focus: N/A
Affiliation(s): N/A

Starting $	Blast/Blitz	Marketing	VA/PA	Publishing
$100	Yes	Yes		Yes

CATEGORIES

- **Fiction:** All including erotica
- **Nonfiction:**
- **Excluded:**

About: IndieSage PR is a one-stop shop for authors. We offer PR, promotional events, graphic design and more!

TOUR ORGANIZERS

Indigo Marketing & Design (T9-036)

http://indigomarketingdesign.com/
Tour Information: http://indigomarketingdesign.com/tour-hosts/
Special Focus: N/A
Affiliation(s): N/A

Starting $	Blast/Blitz	Marketing	VA/PA	Publishing
$50	Yes		Yes	Yes

CATEGORIES
- **Fiction:** Inquire
- **Nonfiction:**
- **Excluded:**

About: IndiGo's team provides editorial support, book design services, and a range of marketing services in addition to organizing blog tours for reviews.

iRead Book Tours (T9-005)

http://www.ireadbooktours.com/
Tour Information: http://www.
ireadbooktours.com/tour-packages.html
Special Focus: N/A
Affiliation(s): N/A

Starting $	Blast/Blitz	Marketing	VA/PA	Publishing
$99		Yes		

CATEGORIES
- **Fiction:** Most accepted, children through adult
- **Nonfiction:**
- **Excluded:** Horror or occult, or books labeled LGBT. These elements can be present, but not the theme. Inquire if unsure.

About: Laura Fabiani has been in the book publicity arena for 10 years. She has been blogging about books and writing reviews since 2009. She understands the book blogging community well and what indie and small press authors are looking for. She guarantees reviews with her tours, offers customer service through phone chats and follows up on all correspondence. More info here: https://youtu.be/Zuz6gcZzbeo

TOUR ORGANIZERS

Italy Book Tours (T9-006)

http://www.italybooktours.com
Tour Information: http://www.italybooktours.com
Special Focus: N/A
Affiliation(s): N/A

Starting $	Blast/Blitz	Marketing	VA/PA	Publishing
$99		Yes		

CATEGORIES

- **Fiction:** Most accepted, children through adult
- **Nonfiction:**
- **Excluded:** Horror or occult, or books labeled LGBT. These elements can be present, but not the theme. Inquire if unsure.

About: Laura Fabiani has been in the book publicity arena for 10 years. She has been blogging about books and writing reviews since 2009. She understands the book blogging community well and what indie and small press authors are looking for. She guarantees reviews with her tours, offers customer service through phone chats and follows up on all correspondence. More info here: https://youtu.be/Zuz6gcZzbeo

TOUR ORGANIZERS

Tilton's Author Services

http://katetilton.com/
Tour Information:
https://katetilton.com/author-services/
Special Focus: N/A
Affiliation(s): N/A

Starting $	Blast/Blitz	Marketing	VA/PA	Publishing
$105		Yes	Yes	

CATEGORIES
- **Fiction:** All
- **Nonfiction:**
- **Excluded:** Erotica, Mature Romance

About: I designed the reach-out to be a more flexible option for authors and bloggers than a standard blog tour. I have been serving authors since 2010. Founder of Kate Tilton's Author Services, LLC, I help authors of all stripes upscale their businesses and connect with readers. I loves cats, tea, and all geeky things.

Lady Amber's Reviews & PR (T9-007)

http://www.ladyambersreviews.com
Tour Information: http://tinyurl.com/y76rso3g
Special Focus: N/A
Affiliation(s): N/A

Starting $	Blast/Blitz	Marketing	VA/PA	Publishing
$30		Yes	Yes	

CATEGORIES
- **Fiction:** All including erotica
- **Nonfiction:**
- **Excluded:**

About: Lady Amber's Reviews & PR offers several affordable packages to suit needs of all authors and publishers. I work with a variety of genre, and have several hundred bloggers that love to support new and seasoned authors.

TOUR ORGANIZERS

Lola's Blog Tours (T9-020)

http://www.lolasblogtours.net
Tour Information: http://www.lolasblogtours.net/services/
Special Focus: N/A
Affiliation(s): N/A

Starting $	Blast/Blitz	Marketing	VA/PA	Publishing
$140	Yes			

CATEGORIES

- **Fiction:** Adult, Middle Grade, NA, YA
- **Nonfiction:**
- **Excluded:** Nonfiction

About: I love reading and everything surrounding books. I enjoy working with authors to make their books a success. I also write blogs posts aimed at authors about book marketing and more on my blog. I find book marketing very interesting and try and stay up to date about the latest trends and ways to promote books.

Lone Star Book Publicity (T9-037)

https://www.lonestarpublicity.com/
Tour Information: https://www.lonestarpublicity.com/book-blog-tours
Special Focus: Texas: books with a connection to Texas.
Affiliation(s): N/A

Starting $	Blast/Blitz	Marketing	VA/PA	Publishing
$99	Yes	Yes		

CATEGORIES

- **Fiction:** Texas-centric/related only
- **Nonfiction:** Texas-centric/related only
- **Excluded:** Books unrelated to Texas.

About: Lone Star Book Publicity helps authors promote Texas-related books.

TOUR ORGANIZERS

Magic of Books Promotions (T9-038)

http://magicofbookspromo.blogspot.com/
Tour Information: http://tinyurl.com/y9nfugrn
Special Focus: N/A
Affiliation(s): N/A

Starting $	Blast/Blitz	Marketing	VA/PA	Publishing
$60	Yes			

CATEGORIES
- **Fiction:** Inquire
- **Nonfiction:**
- **Excluded:**

About: Magic of Books Promotions assists authors with book releases, promoting already published books, and promoting the author him or herself. Note: there will be a price change effective January 1, 2018.

Once Upon An Alpha (T9-021)

http://onceuponanalpha.com
Tour Information: https://onceuponanalpha.com/author-promotions/
Special Focus: N/A
Affiliation(s): N/A

Starting $	Blast/Blitz	Marketing	VA/PA	Publishing
$175	Yes			

CATEGORIES
- **Fiction:** Romance
- **Nonfiction:** Cookbooks
- **Excluded:** Biography, Nonfiction, Religion

About: We started in June 2014. We love all things romance and bookish.

Partners in Crime (T9-022)

http://www.partnersincrimetours.net
Tour Information: http://www.
partnersincrimetours.net/tour-options/
Special Focus: Crime, mystery, thriller
Affiliation(s): N/A

Starting $	Blast/Blitz	Marketing	VA/PA	Publishing
$275	Yes			

CATEGORIES

- **Fiction:** Crime, Mystery, Suspense
- **Nonfiction:**
- **Excluded:** All except Mystery/Suspense

About: Partners In Crime Tours started in 2011 and have been organizing tours for several publishers, publicists and authors.

Prism Book Tours (T9-023)

http://prismbooktours.blogspot.com/
Tour Information: http://tinyurl.com/ycfaahye
Special Focus: N/A
Affiliation(s): N/A

Starting $	Blast/Blitz	Marketing	VA/PA	Publishing
$30	Yes			

CATEGORIES

- **Fiction:** Adult, Fantasy, Middle Grade, NA, Romance, Science Fiction, YA
- **Nonfiction:**
- **Excluded:** Children's, Erotica, Horror, Nonfiction

About: Laura and Tressa both have years of book blogging and promotional tour experience. Our goal is to provide affordable options to authors and publishers for promoting their books, while also adding creative touring. We both still love reading and sharing about the books we love on our own book blogs. Laura can be found at burgandyice.blogspot.com and Tressa at www. wishfulendings.com.

TOUR ORGANIZERS

Providence Book Promotions (T9-024)

http://www.providenceBookpromotions.com
Tour Information: http://tinyurl.com/yc6t7wcd
Special Focus: N/A
Affiliation(s): N/A

Starting $	Blast/Blitz	Marketing	VA/PA	Publishing
$275	Yes			

CATEGORIES

- **Fiction:** All except Mystery/Suspense
- **Nonfiction:**
- **Excluded:** Erotica, Mystery, Suspense

About: Providence Book Promotions, a subsidiary of Partners In Crimes Tours, started in 2011.

Pump Up Your Book (T9-008)

http://www.pumpupyourbook.com/
Tour Information: http://www.pumpupyourbook.com/author-services/
Special Focus: N/A
Affiliation(s): N/A

Starting $	Blast/Blitz	Marketing	VA/PA	Publishing
$149		Yes		

CATEGORIES

- **Fiction:** All except erotica
- **Nonfiction:**
- **Excluded:** Erotica

About: Pump Up Your Book is an award-winning book promotion company specializing in virtual book tours for authors. We offer five reasonably priced packages from the Bronze at $149 to the Platinum Plus at $1049, as well as book blasts and book review campaigns. We can coordinate a package to suit your needs as well. We take great pride in the fact that we have set up book campaigns for thousands of authors since opening our doors in 2007 and have had many authors become Amazon bestsellers. Let us help you pump up your book!

TOUR ORGANIZERS

RABT Book Tours (T9-009)

http://www.readingaddictionvbt.com/
Tour Information: http://tinyurl.com/p2s7f4o
Special Focus: N/A
Affiliation(s): N/A

Starting $	Blast/Blitz	Marketing	VA/PA	Publishing
$40	Yes	Yes	Yes	

CATEGORIES

- **Fiction:** All including erotica
- **Nonfiction:**
- **Excluded:**

About: We have been in the PR World for over 5 years.

RBTL Book Promotions (T9-025)

http://www.rbtlbooktours.com
Tour Information: http://tinyurl.com/yabq9ola
Special Focus: N/A
Affiliation(s): N/A

Starting $	Blast/Blitz	Marketing	VA/PA	Publishing
$100	Yes			Yes

CATEGORIES

- **Fiction:** All
- **Nonfiction:** Memoirs
- **Excluded:** Children's, Christian Literature, Middle Grade

About: I have been coordinating virtual tours for 5 yrs. now it is a passion of mine.

TOUR ORGANIZERS

Rockstar Book Tours (T9-040)

http://www.rockstarbooktours.com/
Tour Information: http://tinyurl.com/ydzbwomn
Special Focus: N/A
Affiliation(s): N/A

Starting $	Blast/Blitz	Marketing	VA/PA	Publishing
$50				

CATEGORIES

- **Fiction:** Paranormal Romance, Urban Fantasy, YA
- **Nonfiction:**
- **Excluded:** Adult Contemporary Romance, Erotica, Middle Grade, Nonfiction, Picture Books

About: The Rockstar Book Tours team-of-two organizes book tours, cover and trailer reveals, and manages scavenger hunt giveaway tours. Books are also promoted on one or both of the owner's websites.

TOUR ORGANIZERS

Sage's Blog Tours (T9-010)

http://www.sagesblogtours.com/
Tour Information:
http://www.sagesblogtours.com/our-services.html
Special Focus: N/A

Affiliation(s): N/A

Starting $	Blast/Blitz	Marketing	VA/PA	Publishing
$50	Yes	Yes		Yes

CATEGORIES

- **Fiction:** All including erotica
- **Nonfiction:**
- **Excluded:**

About: Sage's Blog Tours is a full-service pre-press and promotional company that works with authors of all genres. We offer services to construct your book, as well as help promote your work in a fun and successful way. From author coaching to design critique to virtual blog tours—we do it all!

Our in-house graphic designer is exceptional at book formatting, cover design, and creating promotional tools for your online tour and in-person events. Additionally, we have an excellent team of bloggers who are ready to work with you on your book.

TOUR ORGANIZERS

Silver Dagger Book Tours (T9-011)

http://silver-dagger-scriptorium.weebly.com/
Tour Information: http://tinyurl.com/y87el58g
Special Focus: N/A
Affiliation(s): N/A

Starting $	Blast/Blitz	Marketing	VA/PA	Publishing
Offer		Yes		

CATEGORIES

- **Fiction:** All including erotica
- **Nonfiction:**
- **Excluded:** Nonfiction

About: I'm an experienced book blogger and have been running my own tours since September of 2016. As of September of 2017, I've now successfully run almost 400 tours now and usually have two tours kick off every weekday and even a few on the weekends! I have a spectacular group of bloggers that love to share my tours and will blast social media to get the word out about the books. Each tour has a mix of spotlights, guest posts, excerpts and reviews. I love to make custom graphics for my tours where everything flows beautifully and really take the time and care to make sure everything is just right.

What's the cost of all this? YOU PAY WHAT YOU WANT! That's right, I do not have set rates, instead you pay whatever you can comfortably afford and what you feel is fair for all my hard work AFTER the tour is over and you're happy with everything. I like to ensure that everybody is pleased with the tour and gets the results you were expecting.

I accept ALL fictional genres, whether it's fantasy, horror, romance, erotica, historical, scifi, thriller, mystery, MG, YA, NA, LGBT, or any other genre out there! As long as it's fictional, I'll do a tour for you! I also do tour children's books as well sometimes, though those have a smaller audience as most bloggers prefer teen or adult books. I adore series and love to tour the entire series if possible, no matter how many books are included. Indie authors, published authors and publishing companies are welcome! I work with several large publishing companies a few times a month and they're all extremely pleased with my results. Contact me to work out rates for publishers needing multiple tours.

So if you have a book that needs promo and need a tour, please get a hold of me! I'm completely affordable to everybody and accept all genres!

TOUR ORGANIZERS

Spunky N Sassy (T9-026)

http://spunky-n-sassy.blogspot.com/
Tour Information: http://tinyurl.com/yc7evwon
Special Focus: N/A
Affiliation(s): N/A

Starting $	Blast/Blitz	Marketing	VA/PA	Publishing
$0				

CATEGORIES

- **Fiction:** Dystopian, Paranormal, Romance
- **Nonfiction:**
- **Excluded:** Crime, Erotica, Nonfiction, Suspense

About: I started as a admin to this site and have since become the sole proprietor.

The Audiobookworm (T9-013)

http://theaudiobookworm.com/
Tour Information: https://audiobookwormpromotions.com/tours/
Special Focus: Audiobooks, exclusively
Affiliation(s): N/A

Starting $	Blast/Blitz	Marketing	VA/PA	Publishing
$3.35/stop		Yes		Yes

CATEGORIES

- **Fiction:** Touring
- **Nonfiction:** Touring
- **Excluded:** None

About: Audiobookworm Promotions' goal is to provide authors, publishers, and narrators of audiobooks with services comparable to those available to the traditional book format.

TOUR ORGANIZERS

The Book Garden PR (T9-027)

http://theBookgardenpr.com
Tour Information: http://www.theBookgardenpr.com/authorservices
Special Focus: N/A
Affiliation(s): N/A

Starting $	Blast/Blitz	Marketing	VA/PA	Publishing
$50	Yes		Yes	Yes

CATEGORIES

- **Fiction:** Erotica, Mystery, Paranormal, Romance, Thriller
- **Nonfiction:**
- **Excluded:** Children's, Memoirs, Nonfiction

About: Starting off book blogging four years ago and after many years of coordinating my tours and giveaways, I decided to turn my hobby into a business so the Book Garden was born.

The YP Publishing (T9-028)

http://theyppublishing.com/
Tour Information: http://theyppublishing.com/booktours/
Special Focus: Nonfiction Virtual Book Tours
Affiliation(s): N/A

Starting $	Blast/Blitz	Marketing	VA/PA	Publishing
$360		Yes	Yes	Yes

CATEGORIES

- **Fiction:** Inquire
- **Nonfiction:**
- **Excluded:** Erotica

About: Services that meet the needs of Services that meet the needs of authors and speakers.

TOUR ORGANIZERS

Ultimate Fantasy Books (T9-042)

https://www.ultimatefantasybooks.com/
Tour Information: https://www.
ultimatefantasybooks.com/book-tours.php
Special Focus: N/A
Affiliation(s): N/A

Starting $	Blast/Blitz	Marketing	VA/PA	Publishing
$35		Yes	Yes	Yes

CATEGORIES

- **Fiction:** Inquire
- **Nonfiction:**
- **Excluded:**

About: Ultimate Fantasy Books offers a range of services, including but not limited to: blog tours, book blitzes, cover reveals, booktrailer creation, and book cover design.

Write Now Literary (T9-029)

http://www.wnlbooktours.com
Tour Information: http://wnlbooktours.com/virtual-tour-packages/
Special Focus: N/A
Affiliation(s): N/A

Starting $	Blast/Blitz	Marketing	VA/PA	Publishing
$150	Yes			

CATEGORIES

- **Fiction:** Children's, Christian Fiction, Contemporary Romance, Fiction, Historical Fiction, YA
- **Nonfiction:** Memoirs, Self-Help
- **Excluded:** Erotica, Horror, LGBT, Science Fiction

About: I'm passionate about helping authors build an audience and platform.

TOUR ORGANIZERS

Writerly Yours (T9-030)

http://writerlyyoursco.blogspot.com
Tour Information: http://www.writerlyyours.
com/p/author-sign-up.html
Special Focus: N/A
Affiliation(s): N/A

Starting $	Blast/Blitz	Marketing	VA/PA	Publishing
Inquire	Yes	Yes		Yes

CATEGORIES

- **Fiction:** Children's Fiction, Clean Romance, Middle Grade, Mystery, Science Fiction, Teen Fiction, Women's Fiction, YA
- **Nonfiction:**
- **Excluded:** Adult Fiction, Crime, Dystopian, Erotica, Horror, Paranormal

About: I started Writerly Yours after three years of blogging and a year of writing and publishing when I realized how helpful bloggers and writers can be for each other if there's a platform to connect. I help by providing custom PR and branding solutions at affordable prices. Sometimes for free.

TOUR ORGANIZERS

Xpresso Book Tours (T9-012)

http://xpressobooktours.com/
Tour Information:
http://xpressobooktours.com/services/
Special Focus: N/A

Affiliation(s): N/A

Starting $	Blast/Blitz	Marketing	VA/PA	Publishing
$120		Yes		

CATEGORIES

- **Fiction:** All including erotica
- **Nonfiction:**
- **Excluded:**

About: Xpresso Book Tours is run by Giselle of Xpresso Reads who has been part of the blogging community since September 2011 and started Xpresso Book Tours in October 2012. Currently, Xpresso Book Tours has successfully completed over 700 blog tours and 2,500 promotional events.

Background: Giselle has 14 years experience in customer relations and client service, 6 years in web design (16 years in Photoshop/graphic design), and 6 years in Public Relations. She graduated top-tier of her class with a bachelor's degree in Business Administration. This experience and knowledge gives her the skills to insure Xpresso Book Tours is a reliable and well maintained business.

TOUR ORGANIZERS

YA Bound Book Tours (T9-043)

http://yaboundbooktours.blogspot.com/
Tour Information: http://yaboundbooktours.
blogspot.com/p/services.html
Special Focus: N/A
Affiliation(s): N/A

Starting $	Blast/Blitz	Marketing	VA/PA	Publishing
$30	Yes			

CATEGORIES

- **Fiction:** Contemporary, NA, YA
- **Nonfiction:**
- **Excluded:**

About: YA Bound organizes tours, cover reveals and book blitzes for YA, NA and adult books, specializing in contemporary and YA. Only submissions that are a fit for YA Bound Book Tours will receive a response.

TOUR ORGANIZERS

Part 3
Review
Businesses

Introduction

The listings in this section of the directory are in the business of reviewing books or helping authors connect with reviewers. Several do not charge a fee, but typically a fee is involved.

All the reviewers listed in this section state that they will accept self-published books (or don't say they won't). Just keep in mind that there may be other qualifiers that apply, especially if they do not charge for book reviews. Qualifiers can range from the intangible (the book "looks self-published") to the tangible (they don't review eBooks or POD titles). Advance planning is also critically important, especially if you are targeting reviewers that service the trade—retailers, libraries, distributors, etc.

Paying a company to review your book is an accepted practice. However, you are essentially buying an opinion so reputation matters, especially if you are trying to impress book sellers or librarians.

Here is how we organize them:

TRADITIONAL (NO FEE)

This obviously sounds great, but these review organizations have the highest standards. Make sure your type of book fits their criteria, including their advance notice requirements. Only high quality books with broad appeal are considered.

FEE-ONLY

This is a crowded category with well-known names like Kirkus, but also smaller outfits who have reviewers posting their review directly on Amazon, complete with a star rating. Some may charge more for faster service, but all accept virtually any book you send them.

HYBRID

The accessibility of self-publishing has created a flood of authors seeking reviews. The reviewers in this group have a traditional no fee option, and a paid option sometimes called sponsored reviews. Like fee-only, there is a wide range of names, some on par with Kirkus.

SERVICES

Those in this category are companies that help you connect with reviewers for a fee. For example, BookRazor will sell you a contact list of reviewers who have reviewed books similar to yours. It's then your job to contact them. Then there are services like NetGalley and Edelweiss that operate a marketplace offering advance reading copies to a community of reviewers. It's free for the reviewer, but the publisher/author pays a listing fee to add the book.

(Many blog tour organizers offer a service similar to NetGalley and Edelweiss. Several are free.)

WHAT TO KEEP IN MIND

1. **Budgets.** Most charge, and several charge for faster service. We list the lowest price quoted as of October 2017.

2. **Plan ahead.** With these reviewers it is more important than ever to plan months ahead, sometimes as much as six months in advance.

3. **Quality matters.** A professional presentation is always important, and with these reviewers it may be mandatory. (See the article titled *Impress Reviewers with a Professional-Looking Book* in Part 4, Resources.)

4. **Check what formats they accept.** Generally, whatever you send they will review. If it is an ARC, they may reference that. If an e-Book, they may say they only reviewed the eBook (because there can be differences between print and eBooks).

5. **Review promotion.** As with all reviewers in this directory, the ability of the reviewer to promote their review is sometimes as important as the review itself. Example methods include: printed magazine, their website, mailing lists, social media, Amazon, and Goodreads.

6. **Killing a review.** Several of the fee-only and hybrid reviewers have a policy of posting a review only if approved by the author/publisher. You won't get your money back, but you can at least be assured that a negative review won't see the light of day. As for those that don't explicitly offer this? Ask.

7. **Guaranteed positive reviews.** No firm listed here, or in *The Book Reviewer Yellow Pages* guarantees a positive review. If you discover information to the contrary, please tell us and we will remove the listing from future editions.

Traditional (no fee)

The eight review businesses in this group have the highest standards, and their reviews are arguably the most influential because of it. Several also publish print magazines, in addition to maintaining an active web presence. Those interested in these reviews tend to be institutions and individuals who make buying decisions for libraries, schools, and retailers.

Submissions are not usually recognized when received, nor are authors notified about acceptance for review. That is usually done if a review is published. Books are not returned.

American Book Review

Main website: http://americanbookreview.org/
Submission information: http://americanbookreview.org/FAQ.asp
Lead time/release date: Reviews books published in the past six months, possibly last year.

CATEGORIES

- **Fiction:** Fiction, poetry, and literary and cultural criticism from small, regional, university, ethnic, avant-garde, and women's presses
- **Nonfiction:** Criticism, biographies, and cultural studies; innovative children's literature
- **Excluded:** How-to, self-help

Formats: Print and electronic
About: Printed publication that is published six times a year and distributed internationally. Founded in 1977.

GIVE updates: http://breve.link/e9give   GET updates: http://breve.link/e9get

BookLife (Publishers Weekly)

Main website: https://booklife.com/

Submission information: https://booklife.com/about-us/review-submission-guidelines.html

Lead time/release date: Reviews, if selected, take 6-12 weeks. Selection for a review does not mean the review will be published. A reason will not be provided if a book is not selected for review.

CATEGORIES

- **Fiction:** None specifically excluded
- **Nonfiction:** Most
- **Excluded:** Reference books

Formats: Print and eBook (PDF and EPUB)

About: BookLife is part of Publishers Weekly and devoted exclusively to serving self- and indie-published authors. Self-published books are eligible for free review consideration and reviews will be published in Publishers Weekly. Like other traditional ("free") reviewers, they stress the importance of quality and offer a free self-evaluation authors can review prior to submitting their book. Besides quality of presentation and editing, books must be widely available for purchase in the United States.

REVIEW BUSINESSES

Booklist

Main website: https://www.booklistonline.com/
Submission information: https://www.booklistonline.com/get-reviewed
Lead time/release date: ARCs are accepted at least 15 weeks prior to publication, but no later than ARCs provided to BookLife, Kirkus Reviews, and Library Journal.

CATEGORIES

- **Fiction:** None specifically excluded
- **Nonfiction:** None specifically excluded
- **Excluded:** Inquire
- **Primary Criteria:** The primary criteria used is whether the book is appropriate for purchase by libraries, and whether it is readily available through standard library vendors (such as Baker & Taylor, Ingram, and Overdrive).

Formats: Paperback and eBook, but eBooks must be easily available to libraries (via, for example, Overdrive, Axis 350, 3M Cloud Library). They also accept newly released videos, DVDs, audiobooks, and children's music CDs.

About: Its primary purpose is to provide a guide to current library materials in many formats appropriate for use in public libraries and school library media centers, considering that libraries serve large and small communities with a range of interests. The submission information link takes you to a lengthier description of the types of books they review, those categories being: adult, youth, graphic novels, audio-visual media, and reference resources. Booklist is a publication of the American Library Association.

Historical Novel Society

Main website: https://historicalnovelsociety.org/
Submission information: https://historicalnovelsociety.org/our-reviews/
submitting-books-for-review/
Lead time/release date: Books published within the last year, submitted
as early as possible.

CATEGORIES

- **Fiction:** Any historical fiction; books set 50+ years in the past
- **Nonfiction:** N/A
- **Excluded:** Inquire

Formats: Print and eBook
About: The Historical Novel Society (HNS) has a print publication where
selected reviews appear, but all reviews are published online. Membership
is not relevant in the selection process. However, beginning in 2017 HNS
established a new section in the print edition called "Members' New Books"
where member books are listed. These are not reviews, only mentions. You
need to be a member and you need to notify HNS about your book.

REVIEW BUSINESSES

Library Journal

Main website: http://reviews.libraryjournal.com/
Submission information: http://reviews.libraryjournal.com/about/submitting-titles-for-review/
Lead time/release date: They prefer to receive ARCs three to four months prior to publication date. Certain reference and heavily illustrated books may be considered if submitted later than the date of publication. See the list on the submission information page for categories of books that may still be reviewed up to three months after publication date.

CATEGORIES

- **Fiction:** See above
- **Nonfiction:** See above
- **Primary criteria:** The primary criteria used is whether the book is of potential interest to a broad spectrum of libraries. English language, except they will consider bilingual editions.
- **Excluded:** Textbooks, children's books, technical or specialized works, particularly those directed at a professional audience

Formats: Paperback, eBooks. They primarily use NetGalley to provide digital copies to their reviewers.
About: Library Journal has the highest circulation of any librarian-focused journal, approximately 100,000. Like Booklist, a book that has broad distribution and broad appeal is the ideal candidate. They, too, accept graphic novels, audio, and video, in addition to books in paperback and eBook formats.

Necessary Fiction

Main website: http://necessaryfiction.com/
Submission information: http://necessaryfiction.com/info
Lead time/release date: None specified; inquire

CATEGORIES

- **Fiction:** They have a "moderate emphasis" on short-story collections, novellas, and translations
- **Nonfiction:** N/A
- **Excluded:** Inquire
- As with other reviewers, interested authors and publishers should look at the types of books that are accepted for review before deciding to submit a book for consideration. You can find those here: http://necessaryfiction.com/reviews.

Formats: No restrictions specified
About: Book reviews are published on Mondays, and featured short stories on Wednesday. Visit the submission information page for instructions about submitting a book for review. This same page has a link for submitting stories that meet their guidelines. This past year they have been posting about five or six reviews per month, down somewhat from previous years.

REVIEW BUSINESSES

School Library Journal

Main website: http://www.slj.com/
Submission information: http://www.slj.com/about-us/review-submissions/
Lead time/release date: Two copies of the book must be received at least three months before the month of publication. Books received later than that are generally not considered.

CATEGORIES

- **Primary Criteria:** The primary criteria used is whether the book is appropriate for purchase by libraries, and whether it is readily available through standard library vendors (such as Baker & Taylor, Ingram, and Overdrive).
- They accept children's and young adult general trade books, original paperbacks, reference books, and professional development titles for librarians and educators.
- **Fiction:** See above
- **Nonfiction:** See above
- **Excluded:** Inquire

Formats: Paperback, ARCs, audio and video materials. eBooks, including PDFs, are not specifically mentioned
About: School Library Journal is a monthly print magazine whose readers are school librarians, media specialists, and public librarians who work with young people. Reviews are printed in the magazine and posted online. They focus on fiction and nonfiction for preschoolers through teens. Like other publications for the library trade they review books, graphic novels, multimedia, and digital resources.

Shelf Awareness

Main website: http://www.shelf-awareness.com/
Submission information: http://www.shelf-awareness.com/submis-sionguidelines.html
Lead time/release date: Two review copies are required at least three months in advance of publication date.

CATEGORIES

- Books must be available through national distribution such as Ingram or Baker & Taylor. However, they do not review print-on-demand (POD) books, or eBooks. They have separate contacts for adult vs. children's/YA books.
- **Fiction:** None specifically excluded
- **Nonfiction:** None specifically excluded
- **Excluded:** Inquire

Formats: Galleys/ARCs, and note exclusion of POD books
About: Shelf Awareness publishes two free newsletters about books: one for readers and one for the book business trade. Reviews are included in the newsletters and they also publish an annual editorial calendar you can use as a guide for submitting books. For example, cookbooks are the theme of the November 28, 2017, issue.

REVIEW BUSINESSES

Fee-only

The 12 review businesses in this group represent the most common type of review businesses in Part 3. Prices range from $49 to $425 so it pays to understand what you are getting for your money, and why the services from one review business might be better for your book and goals than another.

Unless otherwise specified, the author or publisher posts their review in the Amazon editorial reviews section of the book's page (via AuthorCentral).

Some paid review services will distribute your book to reviewers, who then buy the book from Amazon (enabling the review to be labeled an Amazon verified purchase). These reviews are posted as an Amazon customer review, the ones with star ratings.

OUR TERMINOLOGY

Fee, Min.: The least expensive review package offered. A faster turnaround is usually available for a higher price.

Kill Option: The author/publisher decides whether to publish the review, or keep it private (in the case of critical reviews).

Amzn-CR: A yes indicates the review will be posted on Amazon as a customer review, complete with a star rating.

Amzn-ER: A yes indicates the reviewer provides you with a written review that you can post to Amazon's editorial reviews section. Note that you are not limited to Amazon and can post or use this review in many other ways, subject to the terms of review business.

Most books are accepted for fee reviews but each service has its own specific policies that must be consulted.

BlueInk Reviews

Main website: http://www.blueinkreview.com/
Submission information: https://www.blueinkreview.com/purchase/
Affiliation(s): Booklist, Foreword Reviews (Clarion)
Review promotion: Website, awards program, social media, and syndicated to Ingram's iPage and Oasis databases. Selected titles are disseminated to Publishing Perspectives, idreambooks.com, and the Douglas County (CO) Library System.
Formats accepted: Print and PDF (there is a handling charge of $19.95 for PDFs to cover the cost of printing the book for the reviewer)

Fee, Min.	Kill Option	Turnaround	Amzn-CR	Amzn-ER
$395	Yes	4-5 wks	No	Yes

CATEGORIES
- **Fiction:** No exclusions noted; inquire
- **Nonfiction:** No exclusions noted; inquire
- **Excluded:** Pornography

About: Positioned as a professional review service for self-published/indie books (author needs to have paid all or some of the cost of producing the book). Extensive distribution to industry partners such as Ingram Book Company forums used by the trade, and other sources used by librarians and booksellers to make informed buying decisions.

Dog-Eared Reviews

Main website: http://www.dog-eared-reviews.com/
Submission information: http://www.dog-eared-reviews.com/
Affiliation(s): N/A
Review promotion: Posted on Amazon as a verified purchase
Formats accepted: Reviewers buy your book from Amazon

Fee, Min.	Kill Option	Turnaround	Amzn-CR	Amzn-ER
$70	Inquire	<30 days	Yes	No

CATEGORIES
- **Fiction:** No exclusions noted; inquire
- **Nonfiction:** No exclusions noted; inquire
- **Excluded:** No exclusions noted; inquire

About: Dog-Eared Reviews also offers five and ten review packages, as well as a subscription service. With a subscription service, one, three, or five reviews are posted each month until the subscription is cancelled.

REVIEW BUSINESSES

Hollywood Book Reviews

Main website: http://www.hollywoodbookreviews.com/
Submission information: http://tinyurl.com/ybzdcg27
Affiliation(s): Pacific Book Review
Review promotion: Website, mailing list, social media, Barnes & Noble, Authors Den, search engines
Formats accepted: eBook, print, PDF

Fee, Min.	Kill Option	Turnaround	Amzn-CR	Amzn-ER
$300	Yes	5–7 wks	No	Yes

CATEGORIES

- **Fiction:** No exclusions noted; inquire
- **Nonfiction:** No exclusions noted; inquire
- **Excluded:** No exclusions noted; inquire

About: Hollywood Book Reviews offers three levels of paid reviews, which differ based on the selected level of promotion. Payment plan available.

REVIEW BUSINESSES

HUGEOrange

Main website: http://hugeorange.com/
Submission information: http://hugeorange.com/shop/book-publica-tion-review/
Affiliation(s): N/A
Review promotion: Reviews are posted on their book press release distri-bution website, www.bookinform.com
Formats accepted: PDF only

Fee, Min.	Kill Option	Turnaround	Amzn-CR	Amzn-ER
$75	Yes	Inquire	See about	Yes

CATEGORIES
- **Fiction:** No exclusions noted; inquire
- **Nonfiction:** No exclusions noted; inquire
- **Excluded:** No exclusions noted; inquire

About: HUGEOrange offers three types of review services: 1) they will send an email blast to top Amazon reviewers and review blogs, 2) they review up to five books for free, per month (limited by Amazon's review policy for un-verified purchases), and 3) and they offer pre-publication reviews like many other reviewers offer. This third service is the one profiled for this listing.

Indie Book Reviewers

Main website: http://indiebookreviewers.blogspot.com
Submission information:
   http://indiebookreviewers.blogspot.com/p/what-we-do.html
Affiliation(s): N/A
Review promotion: Posted on Goodreads, Barnes & Noble, Smashwords, LibraryThing, iTunes, and social media
Formats accepted: Reviewers buy your book (usually Amazon, but also Barnes & Noble or Smashwords)

Fee, Min.	Kill Option	Turnaround	Amzn-CR	Amzn-ER
$120	Yes	Inquire	No	Yes

CATEGORIES
- **Fiction:** No exclusions noted; inquire
- **Nonfiction:** No exclusions noted; inquire
- **Excluded:** No exclusions noted; inquire
About: A service that offers your book for review to their reviewers.

REVIEW BUSINESSES

IndieReader

Main website: http://indiereader.com/
Submission information: See About
Affiliation(s): Clarion Reviews (see Foreword Reviews under Part 3, Hybrid), Edelweiss (Part 3, Services)
Review promotion: Website and Ingram. Top-rated books are promoted on the Huffington Post and to the Association of Independent Authors.
Formats accepted: eBook, print, PDF

Fee, Min.	Kill Option	Turnaround	Amzn-CR	Amzn-ER
See about	Inquire	Inquire	Yes	Yes

CATEGORIES

- **Fiction:** No exclusions noted; inquire
- **Nonfiction:** No exclusions noted; inquire
- **Excluded:** No exclusions noted; inquire

About: IndieReader offers multiple book review options, as well as an awards program and book-marketing services. The following are the two primary review options.

The first option is the typical pay-for-review like others in this category. It starts at $225 and is ready in five to nine weeks. These reviews are promoted as noted under Review Promotion. They also partner with Foreword's Clarion Reviews to offer a combo package that is only $50 more than a Clarion review on its own (slightly more for longer books). Authors and publishers place reviews such as these in Amazon's editorial reviews section on the book listing page. More information can be found at this link: http://indiereader.com/indie-book-reviews/

The second option is for authors who would rather have Amazon reader reviews—these are the star ratings that appear below the book's title. IndieReader will sell you a package of three, six, or nine reviews starting at $129 plus the cost to buy your book—these reviews are identified as "verified purchases." Reader Reviews take about four weeks.

iRead Review

Main website: http://theireadreview.weebly.com/
Submission information: http://theireadreview.weebly.com/submit-your-book-for-review.html
Affiliation(s): Library of Clean Reads (Part 1), iRead Book Tours, and Italy Book Tours (Part 2)
Review promotion: Website, social

Fee, Min.	Kill Option	Turnaround	Amzn-CR	Amzn-ER
$65	Yes	2–3 wks	No	Yes

CATEGORIES

- **Fiction:** None specifically excluded except as noted
- **Nonfiction:** None specifically excluded except as noted
- **Excluded:** Erotica, LGBT Romance; books whose main theme is the occult or horror; books with covers depicting nudity

About: iRead Review is part of a family of websites, three of which are referenced under Affiliations. Reviews are priced based on length, as is the time to review. The price shown is for an adult book, 100-150 pages in length. Children's books are less. See the submission page for additional requirements, including the formats they accept.

REVIEW BUSINESSES

Kindle Book Review

Main website: http://www.kindleBookreview.net/
Submission information: http://www.kindleBookreview.net/getstarted.
html
Affiliation(s): N/A
Review promotion: Posted on Amazon as a verified purchase. Also posted on Goodreads
Formats accepted: Reviewers buy your book from Amazon

Fee, Min.	Kill Option	Turnaround	Amzn-CR	Amzn-ER
$49	Inquire	15–25 days	Yes	No

CATEGORIES

- **Fiction:** No exclusions noted; inquire
- **Nonfiction:** No exclusions noted; inquire
- **Excluded:** No exclusions noted; inquire

About: Your book is offered to their reviewers who purchase it from Amazon. The minimum fee noted here pays for two reviews each on Amazon and Goodreads, and assumes the book's price is $2.99 or less. Contact Kindle Book Review regarding higher priced books, or regarding their eight-review package.

Kirkus Reviews

Main website: https://www.kirkusreviews.com/
Submission information: https://www.kirkusreviews.com/indie-reviews/
Affiliation(s): N/A
Review promotion: Website, email mailing list, and 20 licensees such Barnes & Noble, Google Books, Ingram, and Baker & Taylor (but only on websites where your book is available). Select reviews are published in the monthly print magazine.
Formats accepted: Print or PDF

Fee, Min.	Kill Option	Turnaround	Amzn-CR	Amzn-ER
$425	Yes	7–9 wks	No	Yes

CATEGORIES

- **Fiction:** No exclusions noted; inquire
- **Nonfiction:** No exclusions noted; inquire
- **Excluded:** No exclusions noted; inquire

About: Kirkus Reviews is the best-known indie/self-published book reviewer, but they also review books published by the largest publishers—the "Big 5." Founded in 1933, Kirkus provides additional services such as editing, an awards program, author pages, and advertising in several owned media properties including a widely-read print magazine. Books may be submitted at any time, well in advance of the release date or years after their release.

REVIEW BUSINESSES

Pacific Book Review

Main website: http://www.pacificbookreview.com/
Submission information: http://www.pacificbookreview.com/purchase-your-review/
Affiliation(s): Hollywood Book Reviews
Review promotion: Website, mailing list, social media, Ingram, search engine via PR Web
Formats accepted: eBook, print, PDF

Fee, Min.	Kill Option	Turnaround	Amzn-CR	Amzn-ER
$300	Yes	5–7 wks	No	Yes

CATEGORIES

- **Fiction:** No exclusions noted; inquire
- **Nonfiction:** No exclusions noted; inquire
- **Excluded:** No exclusions noted; inquire

About: Pacific Book Review offers 3 levels of paid reviews, each with additional levels of promotion. They also organize the annual Pacific Book Awards.

REVIEW BUSINESSES

Self-Publishing Review

Main website: http://www.selfpublishingreview.com/
Submission information: http://www.selfpublishingreview.com/get-reviewed/
Affiliation(s): BookBaby
Review promotion: Website, mailing list, social media
Formats accepted: PDF, ePub, Mobi, Pages, or Word documents

Fee, Min.	Kill Option	Turnaround	Amzn-CR	Amzn-ER
$119	See About	See About	Yes	Yes

CATEGORIES

- **Fiction:** No exclusions noted; inquire
- **Nonfiction:** No exclusions noted; inquire
- **Excluded:** No exclusions noted; inquire

About: In addition to reviews, Self-Publishing Review offers a wide range of author services including a membership program. Their original review service has three levels and the lowest price begins at $119 with a 14-day turnaround. This review cannot be withheld from publication, but reviews purchased under the other two levels can be withheld (what we call a "kill option").

They also offer a Kindle-specific review service that suggests (not guarantees) a minimum number of Amazon verified purchase reviews as well as sales. For example, the lowest price service costs $339 and promises eight to ten reviews and eight to ten sales. Sales at this level, and at higher levels, could result in a book attaining an Amazon "best seller" designation, if even for a brief period. Be sure to read the extensive terms and conditions on their website.

REVIEW BUSINESSES

Your First Review

Main website: http://yourfirstreview.com/
Submission information: https://yourfirstreview.com/product/book-review/
Affiliation(s): Bar Code Graphics
Review promotion: Website
Formats accepted: eBook, print, PDF, and manuscripts

Fee, Min.	Kill Option	Turnaround	Amzn-CR	Amzn-ER
$149	Inquire	See About	No	Yes

CATEGORIES

- **Fiction:** No exclusions noted; inquire
- **Nonfiction:** No exclusions noted; inquire
- **Excluded:** No exclusions noted; inquire

About: Authors also receive a seven-point report card detailing strengths and weaknesses of the book. Turnaround time is five business days following receipt of eBooks under 300 pages, and seven or more business days for longer books. Printed books take longer due to mailing times.

REVIEW BUSINESSES

Hybrid

There are seven hybrid book review business in this group—companies that offer a limited number of traditional no-fee reviews as well as paid reviews.

The paid reviews generally are for any book, subject to the policies of the business. Free reviews must meet other criteria. Each company has their own guidelines, some of which have nothing to do with book categories and more to do with how the book was published.

As with traditional no-fee reviewers, authors and publishers have no influence or control over these reviews. If your book is accepted for a no-fee review, it will be published. Most of these companies permit sponsored or paid reviews to be withheld from publication.

REVIEW BUSINESSES

Chanticleer Book Reviews

Main website: https://www.chantireviews.com/
Affiliation(s): N/A

FREE REVIEWS

Submission information: https://www.chantireviews.com/book-reviews-for-publishers/

To qualify for a free review, the publisher must publish books by multiple authors, and the authors must not have any responsibility for the cost of producing or distributing the book.

Lead time/release date: Six to nine months before publication date

CATEGORIES

- **Fiction:** None specifically excluded except as noted
- **Nonfiction:** None specifically excluded except as noted
- **Excluded:** Erotica, poetry, books that depict graphic violence or promote hatred

Formats: ARCs, galleys, and manuscripts

PAID REVIEWS

Submission information: https://www.chantireviews.com/book-reviews/
Minimum cost: $395

Withhold negative review option: Yes
Review period: Standard, six to nine weeks; expedited, three to five weeks

CATEGORIES

- **Fiction:** None specifically excluded
- **Nonfiction:** None specifically excluded
- **Excluded:** Inquire

About: In addition to paid and free reviews, Chanticleer organizes writing competitions and offers various author services primarily focused on editorial matters. They also organize a writer's conference and have their own awards program.

City Book Review

Main website: https://citybookreview.com/
Affiliation(s): Reviews are posted specific websites, including:
- **San Francisco Book Review:** https://sanfranciscobookreview.com/
- **Manhattan Book Review:** https://manhattanbookreview.com/
- **Seattle Book Review:** https://seattleBookreview.com/
- **Tulsa Book Review:** https://tulsabookreview.com/
- **Kids' BookBuzz (reviews done by children age 5-18):** https://kids-bookbuzz.com/

FREE REVIEWS

Submission information: https://citybookreview.com/submission-guidelines/general-submission/
Lead time/release date: Pre-release and up to 90 days past release date, then no longer eligible

CATEGORIES
- **Excluded:** None specifically excluded
- **Formats:** Print, manuscript ARCs, eBooks (including PDF)

PAID REVIEWS

Submission information: https://citybookreview.com/submission-guidelines/sponsored-review/
Minimum cost: $199

Withhold negative review option: Yes. It may be traded for an ad that runs on their website for 30 days.
Review period: Standard, eight to ten weeks; expedited, four to six weeks

CATEGORIES
- **Excluded:** None specifically excluded, inquire for more detail
- **About:** In addition to paid and free reviews, City Book Review offers book advertising options as well as author marketing services. Reviews are purchased to run on specific websites (noted under Affiliations).

REVIEW BUSINESSES

Foreword Reviews | Clarion Reviews

Main website: https://www.forewordreviews.com/

Affiliation(s): Foreword Reviews is the brand associated with free reviews, and Clarion Reviews is the brand for paid reviews. Foreword also has a cross-marketing arrangement with BlueInk Reviews for a discounted price (see BlueInk Reviews in the Fee-Only group).

Promotion/distribution of reviews: Website, print magazine, and licensed to book wholesalers such as Ingram, Baker & Taylor, Cengage, Bowker, and EBSCO

FREE REVIEWS (FOREWORD REVIEWS)

Submission information: https://publishers.forewordreviews.com/reviews/

Lead time/release date: Four months minimum prior to the publishing date

CATEGORIES
- **Excluded:** None specifically excluded
- **Formats:** eBooks are accepted but only if there is a print edition. eBook-only releases are specifically excluded.

PAID REVIEWS (CLARION REVIEWS)

Submission information: https://publishers.forewordreviews.com/reviews/

Minimum cost: $499

Withhold negative review option: Yes

Review period: Standard, four to six weeks

CATEGORIES
- **Excluded:** None specifically excluded, inquire for more detail
- **About:** Founded in 1998, Foreword Reviews specializes in indie publishers, including self-publishers (they call them author-owned publishers). In addition to reviews, they have an awards program and offer online and print advertising.

REVIEW BUSINESSES

Lone Star Literary Life

Main website: http://www.lonestarliterary.com/
Affiliation(s): Lone Star Book Publicity (Part 2)
Promotion/distribution of reviews: Website, mailing list, social media

FREE REVIEWS

Submission information: http://www.lonestarliterary.com/promote.html

Lead time/release date: A minimum of a month prior to publication. Inquire for details

CATEGORIES

- **Books must be for and/or about Texas, or by Texas authors. Review submission information for additional details.**
- **Formats:** Books published in digital form-only are not eligible for review. Submit a digital copy with application (type of digital file is not specified).

PAID REVIEWS

Submission information: http://www.lonestarliterary.com/promote.html
Minimum cost: $249/fiction or poetry, $279/nonfiction | Ready in about four weeks

Withhold negative review option: Yes
Review period: Standard, four to six weeks

CATEGORIES

- **Books must be for and/or about Texas, or by Texas authors. Review submission information for additional details.**
- **About:** Lone Star Literary Life focuses on Texas books, for Texas readers. In addition to book review services, authors and publishers can choose from three advertising programs, including classified ads. Authors should also look at the Lone Star Literary Life listing in Part 2.

REVIEW BUSINESSES

Portland Book Review

Main website: http://portlandbookreview.com/
Affiliation(s): An independent licensee of City Book Review
Promotion/distribution of reviews: Website, social media

FREE REVIEWS

Submission information: http://portlandbookreview.com/submission-guidelines-2/
Lead time/release date: A preference for books released in the past 12 months

CATEGORIES

- **Excluded:** None specifically excluded
- **Formats:** Print preferred, but accepts eBooks including PDF and Word documents

PAID REVIEWS

Submission information: http://portlandbookreview.com/submission-guidelines-2/
Minimum cost: $90, eBook only | $100, print only
Withhold negative review option: Yes
Review period: Standard, six to ten weeks

CATEGORIES

- **Excluded:** None specifically excluded
- **About:** Founded in 2010, Portland Book Review follows the same format and model pioneered by City Book Review and is in fact a licensee. The company also offers editorial services.

REVIEW BUSINESSES

RT Book Reviews | RT Review Source

Main website: https://www.rtbookreviews.com/
Affiliation(s): Paid reviews are available from their sister brand, RT Review Source, as profiled below
Promotion/distribution of reviews: Website, newsletter, and social media

FREE REVIEWS (RT BOOK REVIEWS)

Submission information: https://www.rtbookreviews.com/editorial-submissions

Lead time/release date: About four months prior to the publishing date

CATEGORIES

- **Excluded:** None specifically excluded
- **Formats:** Not specified, inquire

PAID REVIEWS (RT REVIEW SOURCE)

Submission information: https://www.rtreviewsource.com/
Minimum cost: $425 for books <450 pages, $500 >451+ pages
Withhold negative review option: Yes
Review period: Standard, four to six weeks

CATEGORIES

- **Excluded:** None specifically excluded, inquire for more detail
- **About:** RT Book Reviews also offers advertising, a paid membership subscription, an awards program, and operates the RT Booklovers Convention (2018, Reno NV).

REVIEW BUSINESSES

The Children's Book Review

Main website: https://www.thechildrensbookreview.com/
Affiliation(s): N/A
Promotion/distribution of reviews: Website, mailing list, social media

FREE REVIEWS

Submission information: https://www.thechildrensbookreview.com/dedi-cated-review-submissions/media-kit/submission-guidlines
Lead time/release date: Not specified

CATEGORIES

• **Fiction and non-fiction literature for children and young adults**
• **Formats:** Print and eBook, including PDF

PAID REVIEWS

Submission information: https://www.thechildrensbookreview.com/dedi-cated-review-submissions
Minimum cost: $195; surcharge for books over 100 pages

Withhold negative review option: Yes
Review period: Standard, four to five weeks; accelerated, one to two weeks

CATEGORIES

• **Fiction and non-fiction literature for children and young adults**

About: The Children's Book Review is focused on children's literature and literacy. In addition to publishing free (traditional) and paid reviews, they publish author interviews and articles.

Services

The five businesses in this section do not review books; they help you reach individual reviewers. Your payment is for a service in the form of access to a network of readers, or in the case of Goodreads, you purchase a book for someone you hope leaves a review.

There is an arms-length relationship between your book and the person reviewing it that goes beyond how other review businesses work. You are basically offering your book, and waiting for someone to read and review it. These reviewers self-select so you don't need to be concerned about what types of books they like.

You have no choice or say about whether a review is posted, or what it says.

You need to be patient, because you cannot control the timetable. Still, the sooner you reach out, the better the chance of a review coinciding with launch date or soon after. Or if you just want reviews, then it doesn't matter when they come in, just that they do.

As noted in the introduction for Part 3, several of the tour organizers in Part 2 offer a similar service. They will add you book to a list, and promote its availability for review to their mailing list and/or website visitors.

Book Razor

Main website: https://www.bookrazor.com/
Minimum cost: $29.99
Author/publisher requirements (what's expected): Provide list of specific books like the book to be reviewed. Contact reviewers to ask if they will review your book.
Review promotion/posted: Up to the reviewer, but since all reviewers are sourced on Amazon, it is expected that reviews will be posted there as well
Formats: Determined by the reviewer
Guaranteed results: Yes

How it works: Book Razor uses the list of books you provide to search Amazon customer reviews of those and similar books. They gather reviewer contact information, send it to you, and you contact the reviewer to see if they are interested in reviewing your book.

REVIEW BUSINESSES

Edelweiss

Main website: https://www.edelweiss.plus/

Submission information: http://www.abovethetreeline.com/drcs/

Minimum cost: $175/month for 1-5 titles*

Author/publisher requirements (what's expected): Manage requests to review books and/or use the settings to control who has access to your book(s)

Review promotion/posted: Edelweiss, and wherever the reviewer chooses. For example, his or her blog, Amazon, Goodreads, etc.

Formats: EPUB, PDF. and MP3 audio files

Guaranteed results: None specified

How it works: Like NetGalley, the Edelweiss Digital Review Copy (DRC) service allows publishers to upload digital review copies and then approve or reject requests to receive a copy of the book for review. Reviewers are a wide range of individuals such as book retailers, librarians, and unaffiliated readers such as book bloggers. Several of the book bloggers in Part 1 reference Edelweiss as a source of books to review.

***Tip:** If you have a single book, a much less expensive option is the IndieReader In-store/Edelweiss Digital Review Copy subscription option. The cost is $149 for six months. Learn more at this link: https://indiereader.com/product/ir-storeedelweiss-digital-review-copy/.

Goodreads Giveaway

Main website: https://www.goodreads.com/
Minimum cost: Free*

Author/publisher requirements (what's expected): Specify how many print books you are willing to give away at your expense. You are also responsible for postage.

Review promotion/posted: Giveaway winners are encouraged, but not required to read and review the book.

Formats: Print only (Goodreads has announced a similar program for Kindle eBooks but it is not open to self-published books at this time.)

Guaranteed results: No

How it works: Books can be offered by the author, publisher, or publicist. You choose a specific time period and the country or countries to target, and Goodreads promotes the giveaway. When the period ends, Goodreads randomly selects the winners and sends you a mailing list. You mail the books at your expense and no further contact with the winners is allowed.

Books may be offered at any time; in advance of the release date or after their release.

*Goodreads does not charge a fee, but the author has to provide the books and pay to delivery them.

REVIEW BUSINESSES

NetGalley

Main website: https://www.netgalley.com/
Submission information: https://netgalley.uservoice.com/knowledgebase/articles/105722-do-you-work-with-individual-authors
Minimum cost: $450/6-month listing*

Author/publisher requirements (what's expected): Manage requests to review books and/or use the settings to control who has access to you book(s)

Review promotion/posted: NetGalley, and wherever the reviewer chooses. For example, his or her blog, Amazon, Goodreads, etc.

Formats: eBook

Guaranteed results: None specified

How it works: Like the Edelweiss Digital Review Copy (DRC) service, a Net-Galley subscription allows publishers to upload digital review copies and then approve or reject requests to receive a copy of the book for review. Reviewers are a wide range of individuals such as book retailers, librarians, and unaffiliated readers such as book bloggers. Several of the book blog-gers in Part 1 reference NetGalley as a source of books to review.

*NetGalley also has an arrangement with the Independent Book Publish-ers Association (IBPA) to offer a three-month listing for $199. You must be a member of IBPA. Learn more at this link: http://www.ibpa-online.org/?page=netgalley

REVIEW BUSINESSES

Story Cartel

Main website: https://www.storycartel.com/

Submission information: https://www.storycartel.com/publishers

Minimum cost: $25

Author/publisher requirements (what's expected): Upload your eBook and build a book page to feature your book. Your book must be available on Amazon.

Review promotion/posted: Readers are required to leave a customer review on their blog, Amazon, Barnes & Noble, or Goodreads.

Formats: Kindle (Mobi), PDF, and EPUB

Guaranteed results: None specified

How it works: This is a co-op style arrangement where readers can download and read your book for free in exchange for promising to leave a review. The book is available to registered users for 21 days, after which they have 7 days to post their review. The author/publisher receives the email addresses of the individuals that downloaded their eBook and can ask them to join their mailing list.

REVIEW BUSINESSES

Part 4
Resources

Reviewer Outreach Log and Checklist

Before you begin contacting any reviewers, it pays to spend some time getting organized. It will save you time in the long run, and help you avoid missing opportunities or making mistakes—like contacting the same person twice, using the wrong name, or not following up properly.

Follow the guidance below to setup your record keeping system. Better yet, we did it for you by creating templates you can download for free. You also get additional sample pitch emails. Visit http://breve.link/e9bonus to get your copy.

LOG YOUR OUTREACH

Keep track of contact date, blog name, URL, contact name, and how you contacted them (email address if email, or note if you used their form). Include a notes field and keep it up-to-date. A next follow-up date is good too.

Use whatever tool you feel comfortable using and above all—keep good notes. Use a spreadsheet or just a table in Word. Both Microsoft and Google have free online versions. Old-fashioned paper is fine, too.

Stay organized.

CHECKLIST OF MATERIALS

Note: You are not going to send everything here to every blogger or reviewer you contact. Send them only what they ask for, and only once you have permission to send it.

The easiest thing to do is have all of the following information in a single Word document. Much of this is also useful if you are the one responsible for setting up distribution of your book. This ensures consistency.

1. Basic metadata (the information that describes your book).
   a. Title and subtitle
   b. Author name or pen name (the way you want it presented publicly)

    c. Publisher or imprint name (if none, state self-published)

    d. ISBN (or ISBN[s], if you have a print book and an eBook)

    e. Release date

    f. Number of pages

    g. Word count

    h. Your book description (edited!)

    i. Book categories*

2. The names of all the books in a series (if applicable).

3. The formats your book is available to read—paperback, hardcover, PDF, Mobi, EPUB, MP3, etc.

4. One or more blurbs, if you have them.

5. If your book is already for sale, collect all those links so you can quickly copy/paste.

6. Links to online references to your book, if you have any. (If not, this is the place to put them when you do!)

7. Links to all your online profiles, as well as current stats (e.g., followers and connections): Goodreads, FaceBook, Twitter, LinkedIn, your website, AuthorCentral profile, etc. By the way, the online currency for many bloggers—how they measure success—are things like social media followers, website traffic, and the size of their mailing list. These bloggers love authors that can help them increase those numbers. An author with the ability to promote the blogger's review may have an easier time getting a book blogger to accept their book than the author who has no ability to help promote their own review.

8. Book covers. Besides a large image (1000 pixels on the smallest side), keep a few others on hand such as 150, 300, and 500 pixels wide. Use a program like https://pixlr.com/editor/ to size your cover if they need a different size.

*Book Categories: The book categories referenced in the Book Blogger section of *The Book Reviewer Yellow Pages* do not necessarily match the categories used by the stores to sell books. Stores, including Amazon, use categories based on recommendations by the Book Industry Study Group (BISG): http://bisg.org/page/BISACEdition.

Handling Negative Reviews

A survey of reviews for some of the most beloved books ever written illustrates a fact of life: no one is immune from criticism. The question becomes how to deal with it, especially in a public setting such as an online store.

In this article contributed by Alex Foster, author of *Kindle Reviews*, he helps us come to grips with the reality of negative reviews, how to handle them, and how to learn from them. This is important advice for all authors.

Alex Foster: You put a lot of work into your book. A negative review can really hurt your feelings, but if you have more positive than negative they won't hurt sales.

Look at it this way: Every wonderful product or book made will generate some negative feedback. It's going to happen. Look up your favorite best seller of all time and it has hundreds to thousands of people that couldn't stand it.

If you get repeat negative reviews, consider taking the advice and changing the source of the problem. Are they complaining about the editing? Maybe the book was too short? Consider fixing the complaint, or adding the known issue to your book description to ward off any additional negative reviews. If you acknowledge a known issue, there aren't any surprises to the purchaser. Your goal is to provide value to people, not trick them.

Acknowledging the issues also voids the legitimacy of any negative reviews you might get about it. If you say in your description that the color red in the book looks pink in some Kindle Readers, any review that complains about the pink color just gets passed over since it was already mentioned.

If you get a majority of negative reviews, consider listening to what your customer base is upset about and fixing it. Remove your offering and rework it. The ultimate goal in creating a Kindle book is to provide value to your readers. If you aren't doing that, you need to go back to the drawing board with your book.

Never communicate with a negative reviewer in any way. It's just a good rule. If you apologize, you are telling future prospects your work sucks and you know it. If you point out how wrong they are, you come across as arrogant. If the negative reviewer responds, you get into a pissing match. Never attempt to communicate with a negative review. It's a no-win situation.

This is such a different concept than the norm in real life. If you have an upset customer, you want to handle it and fix it. Amazon doesn't really provide a platform for doing so. The buyer is always free to contact Amazon to get refunded if they are that unhappy, so leave it at that. Most Kindle Readers have the option right in the menu to get a refund for the book. It's the ultimate solution for any problem a customer would have. There is no need to be in open public communication with them. This isn't bad customer service, it's effective customer service, based on the platform KDP provides. They can express their opinion and they can get refunded easily. Stay out of the way.

You can't please everyone. Even Mother Theresa and Gandhi had haters. If someone legitimately doesn't like your book, it's OK. It's unrealistic to expect everyone to love it.

Ultimately, most prospects know that some people will have a bad experience with your book. Negative reviews are going to happen to any successful book. They aren't all that bad. What is your ultimate purpose in writing your book? Yes, you want to make money, but is your ultimate purpose just to make money? If you wrote a "how to" book, you did it to genuinely help people, right? If you wrote a fiction book, you did it to entertain people.

If you wrote a book titled "How to Do Your Own Plumbing," you may get negative reviews from people saying your book is too basic and just for simple plumbing issues. Those reviews are helping prospects looking for advanced tips to stay clear, while promoting your book to the target market of real beginners. Your book is providing more value because of that negative review. Prospects looking for the basics to plumbing will know they found the right book. That's really your goal anyway, or it should be. You want the people who buy your book to get what they want.

Criticism and negative reviews in general add credibility and help prospects decide if your book is what they are looking for. If your book isn't a good fit and the prospect decides not to buy based on the reviews they read, it saves someone from leaving another negative review.

If you are getting repeat negative reviews about the "it's just basic information about plumbing," consider making it clear in your title, subtitle or description.

A book titled "Plumbing for Beginners" will make a negative review stating "it's for beginners" look silly.

REMOVING A NEGATIVE REVIEW

Amazon has a review policy in place; when a review doesn't follow the rules it can be removed. The review must focus on the book and nothing else. In short, if the review attacks the author or mentions another product or any outside topic, the review can be removed by Amazon. If the review is threatening, obscene, or illegal (like infringing on another's copyright), the review can be removed. Reviewers can't include contact information in a review or any links nor can they mention pricing or shipping information. Also, if the review has incorrect information, it can be removed. There are situations where Amazon will just delete the parts that broke the policy and keep the rest. Amazon enters ⊠. . ." for info they remove. For example, "This book was a great bargain at 99 cents" would be changed to, "This book was a great bargain. . ."

To request the removal or edit of a review, you can email Amazon at community-help@amazon.com. The email you send them needs to be simple and to the point. Include your book title and its ISBN or ASIN, which you can get in the live listing or in your KDP bookshelf. Next, using the keywords below you want to explain why the review should be removed. Finally, you want to provide a link to the review and a copy of the review in your email. Stick to the hard facts and nothing more. If you suspect a reviewer is leaving multiple negative reviews, or if you think it's a competitor, just make mention of it. Amazon can see the IP address and decide for themselves.

Mention the following that apply:

- Suspected competitor
- Someone posting multiple negative reviews
- Mentions author
- Mentions another product or a topic not associated with the book
- Threatening
- Obscene
- Illegal (copyright infringement)
- Contains contact info
- Contains links
- Mentions pricing
- Mentions shipping information
- Review contains false information
- The reviewer is impersonating someone or something
- The review contains advertising, promotion, or solicitation
- The review contains harmful content (virus, bots, Trojan horse)
- The review is libelous, defamatory, indecent, harassing, invasive

Understanding Amazon's Terms of Service

You may have read about Amazon's crackdown on fee-for-review services in 2016. When announced, it created quite a stir but their exclusion of books from the new policy got lost in the message. Here it is again, this time more clearly stated:

[These] changes will apply to product categories other than books. We will continue to allow the age-old practice of providing advance review copies of books.

No one can disagree that positive book reviews on Amazon help sell books. As self- and indie-publishers, the burden falls on us to help make that happen and it usually begins with distributing free copies of our book.

Before Amazon, before the Internet, publishers would haul thousands of advance reading copies of their forthcoming books to industry tradeshows. These would sit in piles, free for the taking, with no requirements that someone write a review, much less provide their contact information.

Accomplishing that now is still possible, assuming you stay within Amazon's guidelines. Here's a look at what's permitted, what can get reviews removed, and how reviewers should disclose their relationship to the author.

All this is backed-up with an Amazon resource section at the end so you can read the fine print for yourself.

WHAT'S PERMITTED

1. Direct from Amazon: "You may provide free or discounted copies of your books to readers. However, you may not demand a review in exchange or attempt to influence the review. Offering anything other than a free or discounted copy of the book—including gift cards—will invalidate a review, and we'll have to remove it."

2. Reviewers can remove, or edit a review after it is posted.

3. Amazon says that just because someone is a friend, or a social media connection, doesn't necessarily result in a review being taken down.

4. Reviewers can submit book reviews for books they did not buy from Amazon. They are limited to five such reviews per week.

5. Direct from Amazon: "Anyone may post comments on Customer Reviews or Questions and Answers as long as any financial or close personal connection to the product is clearly and conspicuously disclosed."

6. A reviewer can link to another product—such as his or her own—if it is relevant and available on Amazon.

See "How to disclose your relationship" a little further down.

WHEN REVIEWS ARE REMOVED

- Never invite (or allow) a family member or someone you have a close personal relationship with to review your book. This is grounds for removing a review.

- If a reader says they wrote a review, but the review was taken down or it was never posted, tell him or her to send an email to community-help@amazon.com.

WHEN YOU CAN GET A REVIEW TAKEN DOWN, OR MODIFIED

If you feel a review violates guidelines, you can click the "Report abuse" link or email community-help@amazon.com.

Examples may include: use of obscenities, a privacy violation, impersonating others, threats, and the usual no-no's; libelous, defamatory, harassing, threatening, or inflammatory statements.

Note: If someone makes a negative comment about your book and you fix it, the reviewer (or Amazon) is not required to change his or her review to reflect your correction.

HOW TO DISCLOSE YOUR RELATIONSHIP

There are many ways to do this, but it must be conspicuous. You can put it at the end of the review (most common method), the beginning, or in the subject line like the first example shown below.

Here is some sample phrasing you can use or modify if you are writing a review, or suggest to others to use if you are asking them to write a review for your book.

1. In the subject line: *I received an ARC for an objective review.*

2. *I received a copy of this book via* [name of source (i.e., Netgalley, Edelweiss, the publisher, author)] *and I'm reviewing it voluntarily.*

3. *I wrote this review based on an advance reading copy that the publisher sent me.*

4. *This review was based on a complimentary pre-release copy.*

Knowing that someone reading an "author-encouraged review" might discount its value, some people will add an additional comment (if true), such as:

- *I've since bought 2 more, one Kindle version for myself and a paperback for...*

- *That said, I liked it so much that I bought...*

AMAZON RESOURCES FOR MORE DETAILS/HELP

Note: you might need to be logged in or have an account to see some of these pages.

1. **Community guidelines**. There are several pages with this title, but with different URLs. From what we see it's the same content: https://www.amazon.com/gp/help/customer/display.html?nodeId=201929730

2. **KDP** has a good resource in their help section. Log in to KDP, in the top menu click **Help**. On the left, click **Promote Your Book**, then click **Customer Reviews**. There you will find several FAQs

and answers, which I summarized previously. But watch that space for any changes in policy.

3. Amazon has a whole section devoted to **Promotional Content** and its relationship to reviews: https://www.amazon.com/gp/help/customer/display.html?nodeId=202094170

4. Most of us sell books on Amazon using one of their book-specific selling tools: KDP, CreateSpace, Advantage, or a third-party such as an Ingram service (one of their subsidiaries is IngramSpark). But you can also sell books via Seller Central's **Marketplace** which has its own policies. Turns out these are the same for books; find them here: https://www.amazon.com/gp/help/customer/display.html?nodeId=200414320

5. **Email Amazon to report problems** or issues with reviews: community-help@amazon.com.

Professionally published books attract more reviewers

If we were to pick a single unifying request, if not requirement, from every book reviewer in this directory, it would be for a professionally published book. But, what *is* a professionally published book? Simply put: attractive, edited, and conforming to accepted book industry standards.

Given the deluge of self- and indie-published books, reviewers can and must make choices where they spend their time. Judging a book by its cover is a start; flipping through a few pages can seal the deal.

Fortunately, there are standards that are not too difficult or overly expensive to reach. To help us in that regard we reached out to Teri Rider, a veteran book designer and member of the Independent Book Publishers Association's (IBPA's) Advocacy Committee.

In her article, Teri highlights the five most frequent issues she sees dividing inexperienced publishers from those who follow industry standards. Following Teri's advice, you'll find a reference to IBPA's new Publishing Standards Checklist and a link to the full checklist. That location also has samples you might want to study.

Obviously, there is a degree of subjectivity associated with such a creative process as writing and publishing a book. It's easier than you think, however, to keep that creativity and still maintain a professional appearance.

Reviewers will love you (and your book) for it.

IMPRESS REVIEWERS WITH A PROFESSIONAL-LOOKING BOOK

Teri Rider: As a reader, when you pick up a book, what do you notice first? Probably the cover was interesting enough to catch your eye in the first place. Next, you may flip the book over and look at the back cover to get a better sense of what the book is about. What do you expect to see on the back cover?

But as an author, you might wonder what *should* be on the back cover? Is there a specific order in which the interior pages should follow?

Recently, IBPA took on the task of defining what the industry standards are for a professionally published book. By following this checklist, indie authors stand a much better chance of getting their books reviewed and, therefore, leveling the playing field when it comes to competing with traditionally published books for sales, reviews, and awards.

Here are the top five issues that can easily be improved to make your book appear more professional.

1. **The cover.** It is important to study other books in your genre and take note of the common elements such as font style, images, colors, and general tone of the cover. If it's a romance, does it appeal to the predominantly female reader? If it is a thriller or detective murder mystery, what fonts do you usually see? Are the colors dark and mysterious rather than pastel and happy?

   One major consideration is that the title be large enough and easily readable at not only a print book size of 6" x 9" for instance, but also at a thumbnail size that shows up on an Amazon search page. My rule of thumb on color is that it should be a color that is found in nature. Neon colors and many web-only colors tend not to translate well to print versions of your cover, so it is best to avoid them.

2. **The back cover and spine.** The common elements of the back cover include a short description of the book (hint: use your elevator pitch), the author's headshot, and a two- to three-sentence bio. This is also a great place to put endorsements or blurbs that are relevant, real, and properly credited.

Look on the back of a *New York Times* bestseller. The blurbs use exciting words and phrases, often shortened and separated by ellipses to express and highlight the review in as few words as possible. Save the longer versions for the first few pages on the inside of the book.

A few critical elements of the back cover are:

- Price, which should be competitive with other books in the same category
- A human-readable ISBN showing the numbers, not just the barcode
- A human-readable Book Industry Standards and Communications (BISAC) subject heading (you can easily search for the right subject at bisg.org)
- Publisher name and/or logo

And the spine should not be overlooked. Essential elements of the spine are:
- Title
- Subtitle (optional)
- Author name
- Publisher name and/or logo

It's worth mentioning that if you have a book with a low page count, like a children's picture book, some POD printers do not allow printing on the spine under a certain width. A book without printing on the spine is a clear indicator of a self-published book and should be avoided at all costs; you will not find books with blank spines in libraries or bookstores. You may need to do a short-run offset printing for a book like this and consider hardcover; in both instances, you will be able to print on the spine.

3. **Title page.** Once the reviewer gets past the cover and gives it a thumbs-up, the first few pages of the interior will make an immediate impression.

The title page should include the title and subtitle (if there is one), the author and other major contributors like an illustrator (again, if there is one), and the name of the publisher with their logo and location. And a small but important detail: the title should match the title font on the cover of the book. The title page is always on the right side or *recto,* and the copyright page always appears on the reverse side of the title page, or *verso.*

4. **Copyright page.** This page is often incomplete in self-published books and this is an opportunity to shine with professionalism. Let's take a close look at the elements that appear on the copyright page; learn how to do it well. According to the Industry Standards Checklist, the copyright page must include:

- **Copyright date and the holder of the copyright.** For example, "©[Author Name], 2017." You can use either the copyright symbol, the word "Copyright," or "Copr,"; all are valid.

- **A copyright notice defining what can and cannot be copied.** There are many standards from short to long. Search online or look in books published by major publishers and choose the one that's right for you.

- **Edition information.** Is this the first edition, a special edition, large-print edition, or another type of edition worth mentioning?

- **Library of Congress CIP data.** Include this information (in full) or a reference to the book's LCCN (Library of Congress Control Number, applied for via Preassigned Control Number [PCN]) at www.loc.gov/publish/pcn.

- **Printing history.** Was the book previously published by another press or under a different name?

- **Country of printing.** This is necessary, especially if the book is printed overseas, to clear customs; not necessary for POD books.

- **Name of publishing company and contact information for that company.** This is important so that someone who is interested in contacting you for things like sales information, or for an editor or journalist who wants to get permission to reprint portions longer than you have allowed in your copyright statement.

- **Name of author and any other major contributor such as an illustrator.**

- **Title of the book.**

- **13-digit ISBN.** You may include the ISBNs for all editions of your book here (e.g., hardcover, paperback, and eBook), as long as they are clearly identified as such.

- **Credits for design, illustration, editing, and cover artwork, as applicable.** Sometimes the interior font used is listed here as well.

- **Any applicable waivers or disclaimers.** This is especially important for works with legal or medical content, and fiction and memoirs.

(An excellent resource for learning about and using ISBNs, barcodes, copyright, and Library of Congress Control Numbers is *Register Your Book* by David Wogahn. It's available from Amazon, the IBPA bookstore, and other online retailers.)

5. **Interior layout.** Interior layout design may be one of the things that stands out most to a reviewer. If you can hire a graphic designer, be sure he or she is a book designer as there are many intricacies of book design that are different from commercial graphic design.

A book designer will likely be using Adobe InDesign, which is the perfect tool for designing a professional-looking book. If you are doing it yourself in Word or Pages, there are things you can do to improve the look, but these programs are limited in their formatting function. Here are a few tips for making your pages look great.

Typesetting. Choose a font that is not Times or Times New Roman. Times was designed for newspapers and thin columns and is not an elegant font to use for books. Some good choices for fonts are: Bembo, Minion, Bookman, Jenson, Caslon, and Garamond. Test a page or two in these different fonts and you will see a significant difference when you compare things like how many words fit on a page and how easily readable one font is from another.

Consider your reader and the genre of the book. The above fonts are all serif fonts and are especially good for novels. Non-fiction books may have things like charts, pull quotes, and sections that need to stand out from the rest of the text, and other font options for these books can include sans serif fonts like Myriad, Helvetica, Futura, Arial, Franklin Gothic, or Gill Sans.

Serif fonts

Bembo:	Here is an example in 12pt used in a sentence. See how it compares…
Minion:	Here is an example in 12pt used in a sentence. See how it compares…
Bookman:	Here is an example in 12pt used in a sentence. See how it compares…
Jenson:	Here is an example in 12pt used in a sentence. See how it compares…
Caslon:	Here is an example in 12pt used in a sentence. See how it compares…
Garamond:	Here is an example in 12pt used in a sentence. See how it compares…

Sans Serif fonts

Myriad:	Here is an example in 12pt used in a sentence. See how it compares…
Helvetica Neue:	Here is an example in 12pt used in a sentence. See how it compares…
Futura:	Here is an example in 12pt used in a sentence. See how it compares…
Arial:	Here is an example in 12pt used in a sentence. See how it compares…
Franklin Gothic:	Here is an example in 12pt used in a sentence. See how it compares…
Gill Sans:	Here is an example in 12pt used in a sentence. See how it compares…

Font size is another consideration. A good place to start is 11 or 11.5 pt; again, test a page or two in different sizes. The leading, or space between lines should be larger in a book layout than in a business letter for instance. You want there to be a bit of "air" between the lines to make it easier on the eyes. I like to typeset books in 11.5 pt type over 17 pt leading. Try it and see how it looks.

11.5/17 The industry standards for professionally…
The industry standards for professionally…

Another finer point for professional aesthetics in typesetting is kerning. Kerning is the space between letters, and this is especially noticeable in larger type such as headlines and title fonts. See the following example:

example:

large gaps   **INDUSTRY STANDARDS**

visually even   **INDUSTRY STANDARDS**

Design. There are a few things you can do to make your interior layouts more interesting, and they are not hard to do. Seeing a well-designed page will get the attention of reviewers much faster than if there is simply type on a page. Here are some ideas to try.

- Decorate chapter heads by using a special font or by adding flourishes above or below the heading.
- Use design elements consistently throughout the book. For instance, use a smaller version of the flourish you used in the chapter head instead of three asterisks when you take a long pause between paragraphs.
- Use a drop cap in the first paragraph of a chapter.
- Use tints of gray behind a chapter head, or above it or behind a photograph. You can also use a pattern if it is not too busy.
- Use reversed (white) type over a gray background.
- For most POD books, you can now use bleeds, where the design can go all the way to the edge of the page without an extra charge.
- If your book has photos, use borders, drop shadows, interesting edges, and angles to add more interest.
- Use page margins that are slightly wider at the spine edge so that when the book is open the reader can easily see all the text on the page. And don't crowd the outside, top, and bottom edges. Use .675" to .875" on the top, bottom, and outside edges with an extra .25" for the inside margin. (Note: CreateSpace's suggested margins are minimum margins—*never use those*. They are too narrow resulting in text that begins too close to the inside (gutter), and extending too close to the outer edge.)

See the following example for the application of all of these tips:

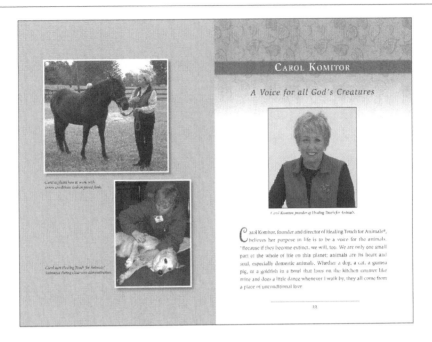

By giving attention to these top five issues and knowing the standards for creating a professional-looking book, you have an advantage over ordinary books that may be well-written, but will be overlooked because of appearance. Independently published books are gaining market share at an accelerated rate and one of the reasons is that we, as independent authors and publishers, are paying attention to these details and producing better-looking books.

To see the entire IBPA Industry Standards Checklist, visit http://www.ibpa-online.org/page/standardschecklist, where you can download the PDF file and also see many examples of the items on the list.

About Teri Rider

Teri Rider and Top Reads Publishing received the 2015 IBPA Benjamin Franklin Awards™ Bill Fisher Award for Best First Book by a Publisher. She currently serves on the IBPA Advocacy Committee.

Teri began her career in traditional publishing, immersing herself in almost every aspect of the business from marketing to illustration, design, and production. Now, after over three decades in the field, hybrid publishing is her specialty and through her company, Top Reads Publishing, Teri guides authors to either self-publish or publish under her imprint.

www.topreadspublishing.com.

Index

Fiction Reviewers by Category

See **About the Indexes** on page 3 for important information about using this index.

Action

Barnsey's Books 24
Olivia's Catastrophe 97
Redpillows 106
The Cosy Dragon 123

Adventure

A Different Kind of Read 16
All the Things In Between 19
Bad Bird Reads 23
Barnsey's Books 24
Book Readers 32
Get Kids to Read 65
Hall Ways Blog 66

Amish

Book Babble 29
Books, Reviews, Etc. 39
Laurie Here-Contemporary Fiction & More .79
Nighttime Reading Center 95

Apocalyptic

Reviews by Cat Ellington 107
Twinsie Talk Book Reviews 129

Bikers

Sammy's Book Obsession 111

Cat-Related

Cat Chat with Caren and Cody 44
Fur Everywhere 64

Chick Lit

Bite Into Books 27
Book Babble 29
Booklove 36
Bookroom Reviews 37
Cindy's Love of Books 45
Diana's Book Reviews 52
Doodles, Doodles Everywhere 54
Electively Paige 56
Jersey Girl Book Reviews 74
Laurie Here-Contemporary Fiction & More .79
My Life. One Story at a Time. 94
Reading After Dark 104
Reviews by Cat Ellington 107
Succotash Book Reviews 119
Walking on Bookshelves 132
Writing Pearls 134

Children's

Beck Valley Books 25
Book Babble 29
Book Explosions 30
Booklove 36
Bookroom Reviews 37
Books Direct 38
Cindy's Love of Books 45
Create With Joy 47
Diana's Book Reviews 52
English Teacher's Corner 59
Feathered Quill Book Reviews 61
Fortified by Books 63
From Me to You 64
Geo Librarian 65
Get Kids to Read 65
Hall Ways Blog 66
Hott Books 68
I Heart Reading 70
Icefairy's Treasure Chest 71
Kristi's Book Nook 78
Laurie Here-Contemporary Fiction & More .79
Mrs. Mommy Booknerd's Book Reviews 91
Nighttime Reading Center 95
POTL Blog 101
Reviews in the City 108
So Many Books, So Little Time 117
Teatime and Books 120
The Cosy Dragon 123
Wishful Endings 133
Zapkode Marie 135

Christian Fiction

A Writer's Journal 17
Book Readers 32
By the Book 42
Electively Paige 56
Emeraldfire's Bookmark 58
For the Love of Books 63
Impression in Ink 72
Jersey Girl Book Reviews 74
More Than a Review 90
Musings of a Snickerdoodle 93
Nighttime Reading Center 95
Seeking With All Yur Heart 112
The Rebel Christian 125
To Be A Person 128

What's Beyond Forks? 132

Christian Romance

Diana's Book Reviews 52

Hott Books 68

Wishful Endings 133

Classics

Always Trust in Books 20

Books are Love.................................... 37

Impression in Ink................................. 72

Livres et Biscuits 82

Nighttime Reading Center 95

The Book Binder's Daughter 121

Clean Romance

For the Love of Books 63

MaryD Reviews.................................... 86

Redpillows 106

Seeking With All Yur Heart...................... 112

Teatime and Books............................... 120

Walking on Bookshelves 132

Wishful Endings 133

Writing Pearls 134

Comics

Reviews by Cat Ellington 107

Contemporary

3 Partners in Shopping 16

b00k r3vi3ws 22

Bite Into Books 27

Charlotte the Book Sniffer 44

Cindy's Love of Books............................. 45

Doodles, Doodles Everywhere.................... 54

Emeraldfire's Bookmark.......................... 58

Firstbooklove..................................... 62

Fortified by Books 63

Imi Reviews Books 71

Laurie Here-Contemporary Fiction & More . 79

Literary Meanderings 80

Musings From An Addicted Reader............ 92

Olivia's Catastrophe 97

OnDBookshelf.................................... 99

Pirate Lady Pages 100

POTL Blog 101

Reading After Dark 104

Reviews In A Pinch 108

Sammy's Book Obsession......................... 111

Teatime and Books............................... 120

The Audiobookworm.............................. 120

The Reading Life 125

The Rebel Christian.............................. 125

Tiffany's Book Blog 128

Twinsie Talk Book Reviews........................ 129

Contemporary Romance

A Writer's Journal................................ 17

Ana's Attic Book Blog............................ 21

Belle's Book Blog 25

Bibliophile Mystery............................... 26

Bitten By Love.................................... 28

Book Freak 31

Brooke Blogs 42

Carly's Cozy Corner.............................. 43

Electively Paige.................................. 56

Ellie Is Uhm ... A Bookworm..................... 57

Her Book Thoughts 67

Home is Where the Wine Is 68

Hott Books 68

Jen's Corner Spot................................ 74

Jersey Girl Book Reviews 74

Literary Meanderings 80

Lola's Reviews.................................... 83

Love between the Sheets 84

Making it Happen................................ 85

My Guilty Obsession Book Blog................. 93

My Life. One Story at a Time...................... 94

Nicely Phrased................................... 95

Red Cheeks Reads................................ 105

Redpillows 106

The Book Disciple 122

The Romance Cover.............................. 126

Up 'Til Dawn Book Blog 130

What's Beyond Forks? 132

Cooking or Food Related

Cookbook Papers................................. 46

Cozy Mystery

Blogger Nicole.................................... 29

Book Babble 29

Brooke Blogs 42

Create With Joy 47

Just One More Chapter........................... 75

Lola's Reviews.................................... 83

Southeast by Midwest............................ 117

Teatime and Books............................... 120

Writing Pearls 134

Crime (also see True Crime under nonfiction)

Always Trust in Books 20

Amazeballs Book Addicts.......................... 20

Audiothing....................................... 21

Author Unpublished 22

Barnsey's Books.................................. 24

Bite Into Books 27
JC's Book Haven 73
Livres et Biscuits 82
Making it Happen.. 85
My Guilty Obsession Book Blog 93
Reviews by Cat Ellington 107
Rocksprings Crafts 109
Succotash Book Reviews 119
The Cosy Dragon....................................... 123

Detective
I Create Purty Thangs................................. 69
Impression in Ink.. 72

Dog-related
Dakota's Den 50

Drama
Books R Us 39
Mallory Reads 86
Redpillows... 106

Dystopian
3 Partners in Shopping 16
b00k r3vi3ws 22
Bad Bird Reads 23
Bibliophile Mystery.................................... 26
Book Babble 29
Book Explosions 30
Bookish Outsider 35
Carly's Cozy Corner.................................... 43
Charlotte the Book Sniffer 44
Cindy's Love of Books 45
Create With Joy 47
DarWrites 51
Doodles, Doodles Everywhere..................... 54
Dreams Come Through Reading................. 55
Fallxnrobin 60
Firstbooklove.. 62
Fortified by Books 63
JC's Book Haven 73
Just One More Chapter............................... 75
Literary Meanderings 80
Lola's Reviews... 83
MichaelSciFan.. 88
MoonShine Art Spot.................................... 90
Read Between the Lines............................. 103
Reviews in the City.................................... 108
Shari Sakurai 113
She Reads New Adult 114
The Violent Vixen 127
TicToc Reviews 127
What's Beyond Forks? 132

Entertainment
From Me to You.. 64

Erotica
Amazeballs Book Addicts............................ 20
Ana's Attic Book Blog................................. 21
Bad Bird Reads 23
Bite Into Books 27
Bitten By Love... 28
Book Review Virginia Lee 33
Caitlyn Lynch, Author................................. 43
Dab of Darkness 50
Dedicated Readers 52
Ellie Is Uhm ... A Bookworm...................... 57
From Me to You.. 64
Home is Where the Wine Is 68
Jen's Corner Spot.. 74
Jersey Girl Sizzling Book Reviews 75
Kitty's Book Spot! 77
Little Miss Bookmark.................................. 81
Lola's Reviews... 83
Love between the Sheets 84
Making it Happen.. 85
Mallory Reads 86
Molly Lolly-Reader, Reviewer, Lover of Words .89
Musings From An Addicted Reader............ 92
My Guilty Obsession Book Blog 93
Nicely Phrased.. 95
Once Upon An Alpha 98
PC Book Reviews... 99
Read Between the Lines............................. 103
Reading After Dark 104
Red Cheeks Reads...................................... 105
Reviews by Cat Ellington 107
Sammy's Book Obsession.......................... 111
She Reads New Adult 114
Shirins Book Blog and Reviews................. 115
Sleep Less, Read More............................... 116
So Many Books, So Little Time 117
The Book Cove.. 121
The Cosy Dragon.. 123
The Romance Cover.................................... 126
Tiffany's Book Blog 128
Up 'Til Dawn Book Blog 130
Urban Smoothie Read 131

Fairy Tales
Bookish Outsider.. 35
Livres et Biscuits 82

Family-Friendly
Book Reviews and Giveaways 34

Icefairy's Treasure Chest 71

Fantasy

3 Partners in Shopping 16
A Different Kind of Read 16
A Writer's Journal 17
All the Things In Between 19
Always Trust in Books 20
Amazeballs Book Addicts 20
Author Unpublished 22
b00k r3vi3ws 22
Bad Bird Reads 23
Barbara's Book Reviews 23
Bea's Book Nook 24
Bite Into Books 27
Bitten By Love 28
Bookish Outsider 35
Booklove 36
Books R Us 39
Brooke Blogs 42
Charlotte the Book Sniffer 44
Dab of Darkness 50
Doodles, Doodles Everywhere 54
Dreams Come Through Reading 55
Electively Paige 56
Emeraldfire's Bookmark 58
Fallxnrobin 60
Feathered Quill Book Reviews 61
Fic Gal 62
Firstbooklove 62
Fortified by Books 63
From Me to You 64
Get Kids to Read 65
Hall Ways Blog 66
Her Book Thoughts 67
I Heart Reading 70
Imi Reviews Books 71
Impression in Ink 72
Jen's Corner Spot 74
Livres et Biscuits 82
Lola's Reviews 83
Making it Happen 85
Mallory Reads 86
Metaphors and Moonlight 87
MichaelSciFan 88
Mrs. Mommy Booknerd's Book Reviews 91
Musings From An Addicted Reader 92
Nicely Phrased 95
Old Fox Reviews 97
Olivia's Catastrophe 97
PC Book Reviews 99

Pirate Lady Pages 100
POTL Blog 101
Readper 105
Redpillows 106
Reviews In A Pinch 108
Shari Sakurai 113
The Cosy Dragon 123
The Howling Turtle 124
The Serial Reader Blog 126
The Violent Vixen 127
Up 'Til Dawn Book Blog 130
Walking on Bookshelves 132

Fiction-General

A Different Kind of Read 16
A.M. Aitken 18
Beck Valley Books 25
Bibliofreak.net 26
Bite Into Books 27
Books are Love 37
Cindy's Love of Books 45
Electively Paige 56
Feathered Quill Book Reviews 61
From Me to You 64
Hall Ways Blog 66
Just Reviews 76
Lola's Reviews 83
Mrs. Mommy Booknerd's Book Reviews 91
Nighttime Reading Center 95
Old Fox Reviews 97
Read Between the Lines 103
Reading for the Stars and Moon 104
Sleep Less, Read More 116
So Many Books, So Little Time 117
The Audiobookworm 120
The Cosy Dragon 123
The Serial Reader Blog 126
The Violent Vixen 127
Women Connect Online 133

Geography

Geo Librarian 65

Graphic novels

3 Partners in Shopping 16
Doodles, Doodles Everywhere 54
Metaphors and Moonlight 87
Pirate Lady Pages 100
Reviews by Cat Ellington 107

Historical Fiction

3 Partners in Shopping 16
A Different Kind of Read 16

A.M. Aitken.. 18
Amazeballs Book Addicts.............................. 20
Author Unpublished 22
Bad Bird Reads 23
Barbara's Book Reviews 23
Bibliophile Mystery................................. 26
Book Readers 32
Books R Us 39
Books, Reviews, Etc. 39
Create With Joy 47
Dab of Darkness 50
Dark Matters 51
Diana's Book Reviews 52
Dreams Come Through Reading................. 55
Electively Paige 56
Emeraldfire's Bookmark.............................. 58
Feathered Quill Book Reviews 61
Fortified by Books 63
From Me to You...................................... 64
Hall Ways Blog 66
Historical Fiction Obsession 67
I Heart Reading 70
Impression in Ink................................... 72
Just Reviews 76
Laurie Here-Contemporary Fiction & More .79
Literary Meanderings 80
Livres et Biscuits 82
Lola's Reviews...................................... 83
Musings From An Addicted Reader........... 92
Nighttime Reading Center 95
OnDBookshelf.. 99
Pirate Lady Pages 100
POTL Blog 101
Redpillows.. 106
Teatime and Books.................................. 120
The Audiobookworm.................................. 120
The Book Binder's Daughter 121
The Book Disciple 122
TicToc Reviews 127
Words and Peace 134

Historical Romance

A Writer's Journal.................................. 17
Bitten By Love...................................... 28
Books, Reviews, Etc. 39
Brooke Blogs 42
Carly's Cozy Corner................................. 43
Electively Paige.................................... 56
Emeraldfire's Bookmark.............................. 58
Hott Books.. 68

I Create Purty Thangs............................... 69
Literary Meanderings 80
Making it Happen.................................... 85
My Life. One Story at a Time....................... 94
Teatime and Books.................................. 120
Twinsie Talk Book Reviews.......................... 129
Up 'Til Dawn Book Blog 130

Horror

Always Trust in Books 20
Amazeballs Book Addicts............................. 20
Bad Bird Reads 23
Barnsey's Books..................................... 24
Bite Into Books 27
Bookish Outsider.................................... 35
Booklove 36
Books Direct.. 38
Books R Us 39
Books, Reviews, Etc. 39
Carly's Cozy Corner................................. 43
Dark Matters 51
Doodles, Doodles Everywhere.................... 54
Emeraldfire's Bookmark.............................. 58
Fallxnrobin.. 60
Fic Gal 62
Hall Ways Blog 66
I Create Purty Thangs............................... 69
I'm Shelf-ish 70
JC's Book Haven 73
Livres et Biscuits 82
Making it Happen.................................... 85
My Guilty Obsession Book Blog................. 93
POTL Blog 101
Reviews by Cat Ellington 107
Shari Sakurai 113
The Serial Reader Blog............................. 126
The Violent Vixen 127

Humor

Barbara's Book Reviews 23
Book Readers 32
Books Direct.. 38
Feathered Quill Book Reviews 61
Hall Ways Blog 66
Home is Where the Wine Is 68
I Create Purty Thangs............................... 69
Redpillows.. 106
Succotash Book Reviews 119
The Serial Reader Blog............................. 126

Irish Literature

The Reading Life 125

LGBTQ

A.O. Chika Book Blog 18
Bitten By Love 28
Book Review Virginia Lee 33
Jen's Corner Spot 74
Kissing Backwards, Lesbian Lit Reviews ... 77
Kitty's Book Spot! 77
MaryD Reviews 86
Molly Lolly-Reader, Reviewer, Lover of Words . 89
Rainbow Gold Reviews 102
Shari Sakurai 113
The Cosy Dragon 123
The Howling Turtle 124
Tiffany's Book Blog 128
Twinsie Talk Book Reviews 129

Literary Fiction

Bibliofreak.net 26
Book Readers 32
Books Direct 38
Create With Joy 47
DarWrites 51
Electively Paige 56
Hall Ways Blog 66
OnDBookshelf 99
Rocksprings Crafts 109
Sahar's Blog 110
Show This Book Some Love 115
The Book Binder's Daughter 121
The Reading Life 125
The Serial Reader Blog 126
Words and Peace 134

Manga

Doodles, Doodles Everywhere 54

Middle Grade

Author Unpublished 22
Belle's Book Blog 25
Book Explosions 30
Booklove 36
Charlotte the Book Sniffer 44
Cindy's Love of Books 45
Dreams Come Through Reading 55
Geo Librarian 65
Get Kids to Read 65
Hall Ways Blog 66
Her Book Thoughts 67
Hott Books 68
Kristi's Book Nook 78
Lola's Reviews 83
Pirate Lady Pages 100

Redpillows 106
The Cosy Dragon 123
Zapkode Marie 135

Military

Nighttime Reading Center 95

Music

Sammy's Book Obsession 111

Mystery

A Different Kind of Read 16
A Writer's Journal 17
A.M. Aitken 18
Amazeballs Book Addicts 20
Audiothing 21
Author Unpublished 22
b00k r3vi3ws 22
Barbara's Book Reviews 23
Barnsey's Books 24
Bea's Book Nook 24
Beck Valley Books 25
Bite Into Books 27
Book Readers 32
Bookish Outsider 35
Booklove 36
Books Direct 38
Books, Reviews, Etc. 39
Brooke Blogs 42
Carly's Cozy Corner 43
Cindy's Love of Books 45
Create With Joy 47
Dab of Darkness 50
Dark Matters 51
Diana's Book Reviews 52
Electively Paige 56
Emeraldfire's Bookmark 58
Fallxnrobin 60
Feathered Quill Book Reviews 61
Fic Gal 62
For the Love of Books 63
Get Kids to Read 65
Hall Ways Blog 66
Hott Books 68
I Create Purty Thangs 69
I Heart Reading 70
Icefairy's Treasure Chest 71
I'm Shelf-ish 70
Impression in Ink 72
Jen's Corner Spot 74
Jersey Girl Book Reviews 74
Just Reviews 76

Laurie Here-Contemporary Fiction & More .79
Little Miss Bookmark................................... 81
Mallory Reads 86
MaryD Reviews.. 86
More Than a Review 90
Mrs. Mommy Booknerd's Book Reviews 91
Nighttime Reading Center 95
POTL Blog.. 101
Redpillows... 106
Romancebookworm's Reviews 109
Sahar's Blog.. 110
Seeking With All Yur Heart....................... 112
She Reads New Adult 114
Simple Wyrdings.. 116
Succotash Book Reviews 119
Teatime and Books.................................... 120
The Romance Cover................................... 126
The Serial Reader Blog.............................. 126
TicToc Reviews 127
Words and Peace 134

Olivia's Catastrophe 97
Read Between the Lines............................. 103
Reading After Dark 104
Reading for the Stars and Moon 104
Red Cheeks Reads...................................... 105
Sammy's Book Obsession.......................... 111
She Reads New Adult 114
Shirins Book Blog and Reviews................ 115
Sleep Less, Read More............................... 116
Stephanie's Book Reports 118
The Audiobookworm................................. 120
The Book Cove 121
The Book Disciple 122
The Romance Cover................................... 126
The Serial Reader Blog.............................. 126
Tiffany's Book Blog 128
Twinsie Talk Book Reviews 129
Up 'Til Dawn Book Blog 130
What's Beyond Forks? 132
Zili in the Sky.. 136

Mythology

Bookish Outsider...................................... 35
Impression in Ink...................................... 72

New Adult (NA)

Ana's Attic Book Blog................................. 21
Author Unpublished 22
Bad Bird Reads 23
Bibliophile Mystery.................................... 26
Book Bangs... 30
Book Freak 31
Booklove 36
Books are Love... 37
Carly's Cozy Corner................................... 43
Charlotte the Book Sniffer 44
Dreams Come Through Reading................. 55
Ellie Is Uhm ... A Bookworm....................... 57
Her Book Thoughts 67
I Heart Reading 70
Imi Reviews Books 71
Jen's Corner Spot 74
Laurie Here-Contemporary Fiction & More .79
Literary Meanderings 80
Little Miss Bookmark.................................. 81
Lola's Reviews.. 83
Love between the Sheets 84
Making it Happen....................................... 85
Metaphors and Moonlight........................... 87
My Guilty Obsession Book Blog 93
Nicely Phrased... 95

Paranormal

A.M. Aitken.. 18
Author Unpublished 22
b00k r3vi3ws 22
Bad Bird Reads 23
Bibliophile Mystery.................................... 26
Bite Into Books 27
Book Bangs... 30
Book Review Virginia Lee 33
Bookish Outsider.. 35
Booklove 36
Books R Us 39
Carly's Cozy Corner................................... 43
Cindy's Love of Books................................ 45
Dark Matters 51
DarWrites 51
Diana's Book Reviews 52
Doodles, Doodles Everywhere................... 54
Dreams Come Through Reading................. 55
Electively Paige.. 56
Emeraldfire's Bookmark............................. 58
Fic Gal 62
Firstbooklove.. 62
From Me to You.. 64
Hall Ways Blog 66
Her Book Thoughts 67
Home is Where the Wine Is 68
I Create Purty Thangs................................. 69
I Heart Reading 70
I'm Shelf-ish 70

JC's Book Haven 73
Jen's Corner Spot 74
Just One More Chapter 75
Just Reviews 76
Literary Meanderings 80
Little Miss Bookmark 81
Making it Happen 85
Metaphors and Moonlight 87
MoonShine Art Spot 90
Musings From An Addicted Reader 92
Nicely Phrased 95
Olivia's Catastrophe 97
PC Book Reviews 99
POTL Blog 101
Read Between the Lines 103
Red Cheeks Reads 105
Reviews by Cat Ellington 107
Shari Sakurai 113
She Reads New Adult 114
So Many Books, So Little Time 117
Southeast by Midwest 117
The Book Cove 121
The Book Disciple 122
The Rebel Christian 125
The Romance Cover 126
The Violent Vixen 127
TicToc Reviews 127
Twinsie Talk Book Reviews 129
Up 'Til Dawn Book Blog 130
Walking on Bookshelves 132
What's Beyond Forks? 132
Zili in the Sky 136

Paranormal Romance
A Writer's Journal 17
Bitten By Love 28
Carly's Cozy Corner 43
Emeraldfire's Bookmark 58
I Heart Reading 70
Lola's Reviews 83
Love between the Sheets 84
PC Book Reviews 99

Poetry
Book Babble 29
Book Readers 32
Create With Joy 47
Empty Mirror Magazine 59
Feathered Quill Book Reviews 61
Impression in Ink 72
So Many Books, So Little Time 117

The Book Binder's Daughter 121

Politics
Succotash Book Reviews 119

Post-Apocalyptic
Shari Sakurai 113
She Reads New Adult 114

Post-Colonial Asian Fiction
The Reading Life 125

Romance
3 Partners in Shopping 16
A Writer's Journal 17
Ana's Attic Book Blog 21
Author Unpublished 22
Bad Bird Reads 23
Barbara's Book Reviews 23
Bea's Book Nook 24
Beck Valley Books 25
Bite Into Books 27
Bitten By Love 28
Blogger Nicole 29
Book Bangs 30
Book Freak 31
Book Review Virginia Lee 33
Bookroom Reviews 37
Books R Us 39
Caitlyn Lynch, Author 43
Charlotte the Book Sniffer 44
Cindy's Love of Books 45
DarWrites 51
Dedicated Readers 52
Diana's Book Reviews 52
Doodles, Doodles Everywhere 54
Dreams Come Through Reading 55
Ellie Is Uhm ... A Bookworm 57
Feathered Quill Book Reviews 61
Firstbooklove 62
From Me to You 64
Home is Where the Wine Is 68
Icefairy's Treasure Chest 71
I'm Shelf-ish 70
Imi Reviews Books 71
Jbarrett5 Book Reviews 72
Jersey Girl Sizzling Book Reviews 75
Just One More Chapter 75
Kitty's Book Spot! 77
Little Miss Bookmark 81
Lola's Reviews 83
Love between the Sheets 84
Making it Happen 85

Mallory Reads 86
Metaphors and Moonlight 87
MichaelSciFan 88
Molly Lolly-Reader, Reviewer, Lover of Words .89
More Than a Review 90
Mrs. Mommy Booknerd's Book Reviews 91
Musings From An Addicted Reader 92
My Life. One Story at a Time 94
Nighttime Reading Center 95
Olivia's Catastrophe 97
On Writing 98
Once Upon An Alpha 98
Perusing Princesses 100
POTL Blog 101
Reading After Dark 104
Red Cheeks Reads 105
Reviews by Cat Ellington 107
Reviews in the City 108
Romancebookworm's Reviews 109
Roses in Ink 110
Sammy's Book Obsession 111
She Reads New Adult 114
Shirins Book Blog and Reviews 115
Simple Wyrdings 116
So Many Books, So Little Time 117
Southeast by Midwest 117
Stephanie's Book Reports 118
Succotash Book Reviews 119
The Audiobookworm 120
The Book Cove 121
The Book Disciple 122
The Cosy Dragon 123
The Howling Turtle 124
The Romance Cover 126
The Violent Vixen 127
TicToc Reviews 127
Tiffany's Book Blog 128
Twinsie Talk Book Reviews 129
Up 'Til Dawn Book Blog 130
Urban Smoothie Read 131
Walking on Bookshelves 132

Science Fiction

A Writer's Journal 17
A.M. Aitken 18
All the Things In Between 19
Always Trust in Books 20
Amazeballs Book Addicts 20
Author Unpublished 22
Bad Bird Reads 23
Barbara's Book Reviews 23

Barnsey's Books 24
Bite Into Books 27
Bitten By Love 28
Book Review Virginia Lee 33
Bookish Outsider 35
Brooke Blogs 42
Carly's Cozy Corner 43
Create With Joy 47
Dab of Darkness 50
Dark Matters 51
DarWrites 51
Doodles, Doodles Everywhere 54
Dreams Come Through Reading 55
Electively Paige 56
Emeraldfire's Bookmark 58
Fallxnrobin 60
Feathered Quill Book Reviews 61
Firstbooklove 62
Fortified by Books 63
From Me to You 64
Get Kids to Read 65
Hall Ways Blog 66
Icefairy's Treasure Chest 71
Imi Reviews Books 71
JC's Book Haven 73
Jen's Corner Spot 74
Just Reviews 76
Literary Meanderings 80
Livres et Biscuits 82
Lola's Reviews 83
Making it Happen 85
Metaphors and Moonlight 87
MichaelSciFan 88
MoonShine Art Spot 90
Mrs. Mommy Booknerd's Book Reviews 91
Olivia's Catastrophe 97
Pirate Lady Pages 100
Readper 105
Reviews In A Pinch 108
Rocksprings Crafts 109
Sahar's Blog 110
Shari Sakurai 113
Simple Wyrdings 116
So Many Books, So Little Time 117
Southeast by Midwest 117
The Howling Turtle 124
The Rebel Christian 125
The Serial Reader Blog 126
TicToc Reviews 127
Up 'Til Dawn Book Blog 130

Short Stories
Feathered Quill Book Reviews 61
Pirate Lady Pages 100
So Many Books, So Little Time 117

Sports
My Guilty Obsession Book Blog 93
Sammy's Book Obsession 111

Steampunk
Bookish Outsider 35
Lola's Reviews 83
Read Between the Lines 103

Suspense
A Writer's Journal 17
Author Unpublished 22
Bad Bird Reads 23
Beck Valley Books 25
Book Babble 29
Book Readers 32
Brooke Blogs 42
Create With Joy 47
Electively Paige 56
Emeraldfire's Bookmark 58
Feathered Quill Book Reviews 61
Icefairy's Treasure Chest 71
I'm Shelf-ish 70
Jersey Girl Book Reviews 74
Laurie Here-Contemporary Fiction & More . 79
MaryD Reviews 86
More Than a Review 90
Musings From An Addicted Reader 92
POTL Blog 101
Reviews by Cat Ellington 107
Seeking With All Yur Heart 112
She Reads New Adult 114
Teatime and Books 120
The Audiobookworm 120
The Book Disciple 122
The Romance Cover 126

Thriller
A.M. Aitken 18
Always Trust in Books 20
b00k r3vi3ws 22
Barnsey's Books 24
Beck Valley Books 25
Bite Into Books 27
Book Babble 29
Book Readers 32
Bookish Outsider 35
Booklove 36

Books Direct 38
Brooke Blogs 42
Carly's Cozy Corner 43
Charlotte the Book Sniffer 44
Cindy's Love of Books 45
Create With Joy 47
Dab of Darkness 50
Dark Matters 51
Doodles, Doodles Everywhere 54
Electively Paige 56
Emeraldfire's Bookmark 58
Fallxnrobin 60
Fic Gal 62
Home is Where the Wine Is 68
I Heart Reading 70
Icefairy's Treasure Chest 71
I'm Shelf-ish 70
Imi Reviews Books 71
JC's Book Haven 73
Jen's Corner Spot 74
Jersey Girl Book Reviews 74
Just Reviews 76
Laurie Here-Contemporary Fiction & More . 79
Little Miss Bookmark 81
Making it Happen 85
Mallory Reads 86
More Than a Review 90
Mrs. Mommy Booknerd's Book Reviews 91
Musings From An Addicted Reader 92
Old Fox Reviews 97
On Writing 98
Readper 105
Redpillows 106
Reviews by Cat Ellington 107
Rocksprings Crafts 109
Seeking With All Yur Heart 112
The Audiobookworm 120
The Cosy Dragon 123
The Serial Reader Blog 126
The Violent Vixen 127
TicToc Reviews 127

Travel
On Writing 98
Amazeballs Book Addicts 20
Bad Bird Reads 23
Bea's Book Nook 24
Bibliophile Mystery 26
Bitten By Love 28
Bookish Outsider 35
Carly's Cozy Corner 43

JC's Book Haven 73
Literary Meanderings 80
Lola's Reviews................................... 83
Love between the Sheets 84
PC Book Reviews.............................. 99
Reviews by Cat Ellington 107
Reviews in the City......................... 108
Romancebookworm's Reviews 109
Twinsie Talk Book Reviews........... 129
Zili in the Sky.................................. 136

Westerns
Books, Reviews, Etc. 39

Women's Fiction
Ana's Attic Book Blog...................... 21
Bea's Book Nook.............................. 24
Diana's Book Reviews...................... 52
Jersey Girl Book Reviews 74
Laurie Here-Contemporary Fiction & More .79
Nighttime Reading Center 95
OnDBookshelf.................................. 99
POTL Blog....................................... 101
Sahar's Blog.................................... 110
Show This Book Some Love........... 115
The Cosy Dragon 123
Up 'Til Dawn Book Blog 130
Writing Pearls 134

Young Adult (YA)
A Thousand Words a Million Books........... 17
A.M. Aitken...................................... 18
All the Things In Between 19
Author Unpublished 22
b00k r3vi3ws 22
Bad Bird Reads 23
Bea's Book Nook.............................. 24
Belle's Book Blog 25
Bibliophile Mystery......................... 26
Bite Into Books 27
Bitten By Love................................. 28
Book Babble 29
Book Explosions 30
Book Freak 31
Book Readers 32
Booklove 36
Bookroom Reviews.......................... 37
Books are Love................................ 37
Books Direct.................................... 38
Books R Us 39
Brooke Blogs 42
Carly's Cozy Corner........................ 43

Charlotte the Book Sniffer 44
Cindy's Love of Books.................... 45
Create With Joy............................... 47
Diana's Book Reviews...................... 52
Dreams Come Through Reading............... 55
Ellie Is Uhm ... A Bookworm.......... 57
Emeraldfire's Bookmark................. 58
Feathered Quill Book Reviews 61
Fortified by Books 63
From Me to You............................... 64
Get Kids to Read............................. 65
Hall Ways Blog 66
Her Book Thoughts 67
Home is Where the Wine Is 68
Hott Books....................................... 68
I Heart Reading 70
Icefairy's Treasure Chest............... 71
I'm Shelf-ish 70
Imi Reviews Books 71
Impression in Ink 72
JC's Book Haven 73
Just One More Chapter................... 75
Just Reviews 76
Kitty's Book Spot! 77
Literary Meanderings 80
Little Miss Bookmark...................... 81
Love between the Sheets 84
Making it Happen........................... 85
Mallory Reads 86
MaryD Reviews................................ 86
Metaphors and Moonlight.............. 87
MichaelSciFan.................................. 88
MoonShine Art Spot........................ 90
More Than a Review 90
Mrs. Mommy Booknerd's Book Reviews 91
Musings From An Addicted Reader........... 92
Nicely Phrased................................. 95
Nighttime Reading Center 95
Old Fox Reviews.............................. 97
Olivia's Catastrophe 97
OnDBookshelf.................................. 99
Pirate Lady Pages 100
POTL Blog....................................... 101
Read Between the Lines................. 103
Redpillows....................................... 106
She Reads New Adult 114
Shirins Book Blog and Reviews.... 115
Show This Book Some Love........... 115
Simple Wyrdings............................. 116
So Many Books, So Little Time 117

Southeast by Midwest 117
Stephanie's Book Reports 118
Teatime and Books 120
The Audiobookworm 120
The Cosy Dragon 123
The Rebel Christian 125
The Romance Cover 126
The Serial Reader Blog 126
TicToc Reviews 127

Tiffany's Book Blog 128
Twinsie Talk Book Reviews 129
Up 'Til Dawn Book Blog 130
Walking on Bookshelves 132
What's Beyond Forks? 132
Wishful Endings 133
Writing Pearls 134
Zapkode Marie 135
Zili in the Sky 136

Nonfiction Reviewers by Category

See **About the Indexes** on page 3 for important information about using this index.

Adventure
Electively Paige 56

Animals & Pets
Book Reviews and Giveaways 34
Cat Chat with Caren and Cody 44
Create With Joy 47
Dakota's Den 50
Epic Book Quest 60
Feathered Quill Book Reviews 61
Fur Everywhere 64

Anthropology
DarWrites 51

Architecture
Doodles, Doodles Everywhere 54
Midwest Book Review 88

Arts
Book Readers 32
Doodles, Doodles Everywhere 54
Empty Mirror Magazine 59
Icefairy's Treasure Chest 71
Midwest Book Review 88
Mrs. Mommy Booknerd's Book Reviews 91

Autobiography
Book Readers 32
Books Direct 38
Emeraldfire's Bookmark 58
Historical Fiction Obsession 67
Just Reviews 76
Musings of a Snickerdoodle 93
Olivia's Catastrophe 97
Redpillows 106
Reviews by Cat Ellington 107
Seeking With All Yur Heart 112

Automobile
Book Reviews and Giveaways 34
Books, Reviews, Etc. 39
Laurie Here-Contemporary Fiction & More . 79

Avant-Garde
Empty Mirror Magazine 59

Behavioral Science
Impression in Ink 72

Biography
All the Things In Between 19
Book Babble 29
Book Readers 32
Booklove 36
Books Direct 38
Bookshipper 40
Booksie's Blog 40
Emeraldfire's Bookmark 58
Empty Mirror Magazine 59
Fangirls Read it First 61
Feathered Quill Book Reviews 61
For the Love of Books 63
Harder to Destroy 66
Historical Fiction Obsession 67
Impression in Ink 72
Midwest Book Review 88
More Than a Review 90
Mrs. Mommy Booknerd's Book Reviews 91
Musings of a Snickerdoodle 93
Nighttime Reading Center 95
Oh My Bookness 96
Olivia's Catastrophe 97
On Writing 98
POTL Blog 101
Redpillows 106

Reviews in the City.. 108
Seeking With All Yur Heart 112
Southeast by Midwest.................................. 117
The Reading Life 125
Words and Peace 134

Business
A.M. Aitken.. 18
Always Trust in Books 20
Bookish Reveries.. 36
Bookshipper.. 40
Dark Matters 51
Feathered Quill Book Reviews 61
For the Love of Books 63
Jersey Girl Book Reviews 74
Lola's Reviews.. 83
On Writing 98
POTL Blog 101
So Many Books, So Little Time 117
Urban Book Reviews..................................... 131

Children's
Bookroom Reviews... 37
Books Direct.. 38
Geo Librarian.. 65
Kristi's Book Nook.. 78
MoonShine Art Spot....................................... 90
Oh My Bookness... 96
Zapkode Marie.. 135

Coloring Books
Fangirls Read it First..................................... 61
Lola's Reviews.. 83

Commentaries
Seeking With All Yur Heart 112

Cookbooks
3 Partners in Shopping 16
Audiothing.. 21
Bea's Book Nook... 24
Beck Valley Books.. 25
Book Babble 29
Book Reviews and Giveaways 34
Booklove 36
Bookroom Reviews... 37
Books Direct.. 38
Books R Us 39
Books, Reviews, Etc....................................... 39
Bookshipper.. 40
Brooke Blogs 42
By the Book 42
Cookbook Papers 46

Create With Joy.. 47
Dab of Darkness 50
DarWrites 51
Dedicated Readers 52
Epic Book Quest 60
Feathered Quill Book Reviews 61
I Create Purty Thangs................................... 69
I'm Shelf-ish 70
Jersey Girl Book Reviews 74
Just Reviews 76
Kitty's Book Spot! 77
Midwest Book Review.................................... 88
Misty103@HubPages..................................... 89
Mrs. Mommy Booknerd's Book Reviews.... 91
My Life. One Story at a Time........................ 94
Oh My Bookness... 96
Once Upon An Alpha 98
POTL Blog 101
Rocksprings Crafts 109
So Many Books, So Little Time 117
Southeast by Midwest.................................. 117
Succotash Book Reviews 119
The Book Binder's Daughter 121
The Cosy Dragon.. 123
Tiffany's Book Blog 128
Urban Book Reviews..................................... 131
Wishful Endings 133

Crafting
3 Partners in Shopping 16
Audiothing.. 21
Bea's Book Nook... 24
Book Reviews and Giveaways 34
Bookroom Reviews... 37
Books, Reviews, Etc....................................... 39
Bookshipper.. 40
Brooke Blogs 42
Dab of Darkness 50
DarWrites 51
Diana's Book Reviews................................... 52
Doodles, Doodles Everywhere..................... 54
I Create Purty Thangs................................... 69
Icefairy's Treasure Chest 71
Midwest Book Review.................................... 88
Mrs. Mommy Booknerd's Book Reviews.... 91
Once Upon An Alpha 98
Rocksprings Crafts 109
Succotash Book Reviews 119
The Cosy Dragon.. 123
Tiffany's Book Blog 128
Urban Book Reviews..................................... 131

Wishful Endings 133

Culture
All the Things In Between 19
Book Readers 32
Empty Mirror Magazine 59

Devotionals
By the Book 42
Create With Joy 47
Diana's Book Reviews 52
Epic Book Quest 60
My Life. One Story at a Time. 94
Teatime and Books 120
To Be A Person 128

Educational
Bea's Book Nook 24
Bookroom Reviews 37
English Teacher's Corner 59
Seeking With All Yur Heart 112
Teatime and Books 120
Urban Book Reviews 131

Entertainment & Gaming
Kitty's Book Spot! 77
Mrs. Mommy Booknerd's Book Reviews 91

Fishing
Succotash Book Reviews 119

Folklore
Bookish Outsider 35

Food Related
Cookbook Papers 46
Home is Where the Wine Is 68
Icefairy's Treasure Chest 71
Mrs. Mommy Booknerd's Book Reviews 91
Succotash Book Reviews 119

Gardening
Books R Us 39
Cultivate to Plate 49
Epic Book Quest 60
The Cosy Dragon 123
Wishful Endings 133

Graphic Design
Caitlyn Lynch, Author 43
Oh My Bookness 96

Health & Fitness
All the Things In Between 19
Bookroom Reviews 37
Brooke Blogs 42

Create With Joy 47
Harder to Destroy 66
Icefairy's Treasure Chest 71
Mrs. Mommy Booknerd's Book Reviews 91

History
All the Things In Between 19
Book Reviews and Giveaways 34
Bookangel 35
Bookish Outsider 35
Booksie's Blog 40
Cookbook Papers 46
Dab of Darkness 50
DarWrites 51
Electively Paige 56
Emeraldfire's Bookmark 58
Feathered Quill Book Reviews 61
Fortified by Books 63
Harder to Destroy 66
Impression in Ink 72
Just Reviews 76
Mrs. Mommy Booknerd's Book Reviews 91
Musings of a Snickerdoodle 93
Oh My Bookness 96
POTL Blog 101
Sleep Less, Read More 116
Teatime and Books 120
The Book Binder's Daughter 121
The Reading Life 125
Words and Peace 134

How-To
All the Things In Between 19
Cookbook Papers 46
Doodles, Doodles Everywhere 54
I Create Purty Thangs 69

Inspirational
Create With Joy 47
Feathered Quill Book Reviews 61
POTL Blog 101

Interior Design
Audiothing 21
Wishful Endings 133

Jewelry Making
Succotash Book Reviews 119

Landscaping
Cultivate to Plate 49

LGBTQ
Kissing Backwards, Lesbian Lit Reviews ... 77
Oh My Bookness 96

Literary Criticism
Words and Peace 134

Marketing
Book Reviewer Yellow Pages 34
Cheryl Currie 45
I Heart Reading 70

Medical
For the Love of Books 63
Livres et Biscuits 82
Teatime and Books...................................... 120

Memoirs
3 Partners in Shopping 16
A.M. Aitken... 18
All the Things In Between 19
Audiothing.. 21
Author Unpublished 22
Beck Valley Books....................................... 25
Book Babble 29
Bookangel... 35
Booklove 36
Books Direct... 38
Books, Reviews, Etc. 39
Bookshipper... 40
By the Book... 42
Create With Joy 47
Dab of Darkness 50
Diana's Book Reviews 52
Electively Paige... 56
Emeraldfire's Bookmark.............................. 58
Epic Book Quest 60
Fangirls Read it First................................... 61
Feathered Quill Book Reviews 61
For the Love of Books 63
Fortified by Books 63
Her Book Thoughts 67
Historical Fiction Obsession 67
I'm Shelf-ish 70
Impression in Ink.. 72
Jersey Girl Book Reviews 74
Just Reviews 76
Laurie Here-Contemporary Fiction & More . 79
Mrs. Mommy Booknerd's Book Reviews.... 91
My Life. One Story at a Time...................... 94
Nighttime Reading Center 95
Oh My Bookness.. 96
OnDBookshelf... 99
POTL Blog 101
Redpillows.. 106
Reviews by Cat Ellington 107

Seeking With All Yur Heart........................ 112
Show This Book Some Love......................... 115
Sleep Less, Read More................................ 116
So Many Books, So Little Time 117
Southeast by Midwest................................ 117
Teatime and Books...................................... 120
The Cosy Dragon... 123
To Be A Person.. 128
Urban Book Reviews................................... 131

Middle Grade
Geo Librarian.. 65
Zapkode Marie.. 135

Military
Barbara's Book Reviews 23
DarWrites 51
Midwest Book Review.................................. 88

Music
Oh My Bookness.. 96
Wishful Endings 133

Painting
Oh My Bookness.. 96

Parenting
Bea's Book Nook.. 24
Feathered Quill Book Reviews 61

Philosophy
Harder to Destroy.. 66
Livres et Biscuits 82

Photography
Doodles, Doodles Everywhere..................... 54
Mrs. Mommy Booknerd's Book Reviews.... 91
POTL Blog 101

Politics
All the Things In Between 19
Livres et Biscuits 82
Oh My Bookness.. 96

Psychology
All the Things In Between 19
Impression in Ink.. 72
Misty103@HubPages................................... 89
Pirate Lady Pages 100
So Many Books, So Little Time 117

Publishing
Book Reviewer Yellow Pages 34
Books Direct... 38
Caitlyn Lynch, Author................................. 43
Cheryl Currie 45
I Heart Reading 70

Lola's Reviews...................................... 83

Railroad
Rocksprings Crafts 109

Reference
Cookbook Papers................................. 46
Impression in Ink................................ 72
Seeking With All Yur Heart............... 112

Religion & Spirituality
All the Things In Between 19
Barbara's Book Reviews 23
Book Babble 29
Create With Joy.................................. 47
Electively Paige.................................. 56
I Heart Reading 70
Musings of a Snickerdoodle.............. 93
POTL Blog 101
Seeking With All Yur Heart............... 112
Words and Peace 134

Science
Booksie's Blog.................................... 40
Dab of Darkness 50
Harder to Destroy.............................. 66
Livres et Biscuits 82
Midwest Book Review......................... 88

Self-Help
3 Partners in Shopping 16
Beck Valley Books.............................. 25
Bookish Reveries 36
Booklove 36
Books R Us 39
Create With Joy.................................. 47
Her Book Thoughts 67
I Heart Reading 70
Jersey Girl Book Reviews 74
Misty103@HubPages.......................... 89
Mrs. Mommy Booknerd's Book Reviews.... 91
Reviews in the City............................ 108
Simple Wyrdings................................ 116
Southeast by Midwest........................ 117
The Cosy Dragon................................ 123
To Be A Person................................... 128

Sewing
Succotash Book Reviews 119

Wishful Endings 133

Sociology
Pirate Lady Pages 100

Sports
Feathered Quill Book Reviews 61
Midwest Book Review......................... 88
Oh My Bookness.................................. 96
POTL Blog 101
Sleep Less, Read More........................ 116

Technology
A.M. Aitken... 18
Book Reviewer Yellow Pages 34

Travel
All the Things In Between 19
Booksie's Blog 40
Cookbook Papers................................. 46
Doodles, Doodles Everywhere............ 54
Feathered Quill Book Reviews 61
Impression in Ink................................ 72
The Book Binder's Daughter 121

True Crime
Book Babble 29
Book Readers 32
Books Direct.. 38
Books, Reviews, Etc. 39
Booksie's Blog 40
Emeraldfire's Bookmark..................... 58
Jersey Girl Book Reviews 74
Just Reviews 76
More Than a Review 90
Oh My Bookness.................................. 96
The Book Disciple 122

Writing
Book Reviewer Yellow Pages 34
Books Direct.. 38
Caitlyn Lynch, Author......................... 43
Cheryl Currie 45
For the Love of Books 63
Tiffany's Book Blog 128

YA
Zapkode Marie.................................... 135

Considers Most Fiction

Bitten By Love..................................... 28   Book Referees....................................... 33

Book Reviews and Giveaways 34
Bookangel.. 35
Bookish Reveries... 36
Booklove 36
Books are Love... 37
Bookshipper... 40
Booksie's Blog 40
Bookwyrming Thoughts 41
Bound 4 Escape 41
Cheryl Currie 45
Crandom.. 47
Crystal's Many Reviewers 48
Donovan's Literary Services 53
Dreams Come Through Reading................ 55
Electively Paige.. 56
Emeraldfire's Bookmark............................... 58
Epic Book Quest 60

Fangirls Read it First....................................... 61
Feathered Quill Book Reviews 61
Hall Ways Blog.. 66
Lady Amber's Reviews and PR.................... 78
Library of Clean Reads................................... 80
Long and Short Reviews................................ 84
Matthew R. Bell's BookBlogBonanza.......... 87
Midwest Book Review....................................... 88
Misty103@HubPages....................................... 89
Musings From An Addicted Reader........... 92
My Tangled Skeins Book Reviews............. 94
Oh My Bookness.. 96
POTL Blog 101
Sharing Life's Moments.............................. 114
The Cosy Dragon.. 123
The Phantom Paragrapher 124
Urban Book Reviews...................................... 131

Considers Most Nonfiction

A Different Kind of Read 16
Bibliofreak.net 26
Book Referees.. 33
Books are Love... 37
Bound 4 Escape 41
Crandom.. 47
Donovan's Literary Services 53
Hall Ways Blog 66
Jbarrett5 Book Reviews 72
Library of Clean Reads................................... 80
MaryD Reviews... 86

Musings From An Addicted Reader........... 92
My Tangled Skeins Book Reviews............. 94
Read Between the Lines............................... 103
Reading After Dark 104
Reviews In A Pinch 108
Sahar's Blog... 110
Sharing Life's Moments.............................. 114
The Phantom Paragrapher 124
The Serial Reader Blog................................. 126
TicToc Reviews 127
Women Connect Online 133

Accepts Non-English Titles

Dutch

Bite Into Books 27
I Heart Reading 70
Mallory Reads 86

French

Livres et Biscuits 82
Misty103@HubPages...................................... 89
Sahar's Blog... 110
Words and Peace 134

German

A.M. Aitken.. 18
Pirate Lady Pages 100

Hindi

Bookish Reveries.. 36
Booklove 36
So Many Books, So Little Time 117

Indian

Booklove 36

Italian

All the Things In Between 19
The Serial Reader Blog............................... 126

Punjabi

Booklove 36

Spanish
Carly's Cozy Corner 43
Misty103@HubPages 89
Oh My Bookness 96

The Serial Reader Blog 126
Urdu
Booklove 36

Accepts Audiobooks

3 Partners in Shopping 16
Ana's Attic Book Blog 21
Audiothing 21
Bea's Book Nook 24
Bookwyrming Thoughts 41
Bound 4 Escape 41
Brooke Blogs 42
Cheryl Currie 45
Cindy's Love of Books 45
Dab of Darkness 50
Dark Matters 51
Diana's Book Reviews 52
Electively Paige 56
Ellie Is Uhm ... A Bookworm 57
Firstbooklove 62
Hall Ways Blog 66
Jen's Corner Spot 74
Kitty's Book Spot! 77

Love between the Sheets 84
MichaelSciFan 88
Misty103@HubPages 89
Musings From An Addicted Reader 92
Musings of a Snickerdoodle 93
Nighttime Reading Center 95
OnDBookshelf 99
Rainbow Gold Reviews 102
Rocksprings Crafts 109
Shirins Book Blog and Reviews 115
Southeast by Midwest 117
Stephanie's Book Reports 118
The Audiobookworm 120
The Book Disciple 122
The Howling Turtle 124
Up 'Til Dawn Book Blog 130
Words and Peace 134

Review Businesses

American Book Review 174
Blue Ink Review 183
BookLife 175
Booklist 176
BookRazor 201
Chanticleer Book Reviews 194
City Book Review 195
Clarion Reviews 196
Dog-Eared Reviews 183
Edelweiss 202
ForeWord Reviews 196
Goodreads Giveaway 203
Historical Novel Society 177
Hollywood Book Reviews 184
HugeOrange 185
Indie Book Reviewers 185
IndieReader 186
iRead Review 187
Kindle Book Review 188
Kirkus Reviews 189

Library Journal 178
Lone Star Literary Life 197
Necessary Fiction 179
NetGalley 204
Pacific Book Review 190
Portland Book Review 198
RT Book Reviews 199
RT Review Source 199
School Library Journal 180
Self-Publishing Review 191
ShelfAwareness 181
Story Cartel 205
The Children's Book Review 200
Your First Review 192

Acknowledgments

This year's directory is comprised of 270 reviewer profiles assembled from more than 5,380 pieces of information, including 467 website links and 114 email addresses. That data had to be gathered, organized, proofed, and assembled into an easily digestible format—and then supplemented with more than 15,000 words of narrative text. It was a mammoth effort made possible by the contributions of these fine people:

Alex Foster, Anna-Marie Abell, Carter Wogahn,
Cherie Kephart, Christine Pinheiro, Julia Drake, Karla Olson,
Kate Tilton, Katie Barry, Kerri Esten, Lalaine Dofredo,
Peter Lichtgarn, Teri Rider, and Valerie Nemeth.

Thank you again to everyone mentioned here, as well as our book bloggers and tour organizers, for all your contributions.

David Wogahn
Publisher
The Book Reviewer Yellow Pages

About *The Book Reviewer Yellow Pages*

The Book Reviewer Yellow Pages is the only comprehensive source of influential book reviewer profiles and book review guidance available to authors, small publishers, and publicists. This book contains the time-tested guidance you need to zero-in on the reviewers who will be interested in your book. It is published by PartnerPress, in association with professional self-publishing services company AuthorImprints, a member of the Independent Book Publishers Association and the Alliance of Independent Authors.

BookReviewerYellowPages.com

AuthorImprints.com